DREADNOUGHTS
IN CAMERA

DREADNOUGHTS
IN CAMERA
BUILDING THE DREADNOUGHTS

1905–1920

ROGER D. THOMAS and BRIAN PATTERSON

with line drawings by

BRIAN PATTERSON

A Budding Book

This book was first published in 1998 by
Sutton Publishing Limited
in association with The Royal Naval Museum

This edition first published in 2000 by Budding Books, an imprint of
Sutton Publishing Limited
Phoenix Mill · Thrupp · Stroud · Gloucestershire · GL5 2BU

A catalogue record for this book is available from the British Library

ISBN 1-84015-108-0

Typeset in 11/15pt Baskerville
Typesetting and origination by
Sutton Publishing Limited.
Printed in Great Britain by
Redwood Books, Trowbridge, Wiltshire.

CONTENTS

Acknowledgements   vii

Introduction: Photographic Images as Representational Documents   ix

Abbreviations   xi

1: The Dreadnought Programme   1

2: Preparatory Work   13

3: The Building Slip   26

4: Launching Dreadnoughts   52

5: Fitting-Out: Superstructure, Propulsion and Armaments   74

6: Commissioning, Sea and Gunnery Trials   116

7: Epilogue   132

Alphabetical List of Dreadnoughts   135

Appendix   136

Bibliography   176

Dreadnought Bibliography   178

Index   179

ACKNOWLEDGEMENTS

The author's interest in the photographic images of Dreadnoughts began with the discovery of the Pescott Frost collection of photographs in Portsmouth Central Library during the early 1980s. This initially led to the exhibition in October 1985 'We Want Eight, Portsmouth and the Dreadnoughts 1905–1916'. Several years later a more ambitious exhibition was produced, entitled 'The Building of the Great Fleet, British Dreadnoughts 1905–1920'. The exhibition was supported by the University of Portsmouth, the Portsmouth Naval Base Property Trust, Portsmouth City Council, Hampshire County Council and John Brown plc. Many of the images came from the qualitative photographic records kept at the Business Record Centre, University of Glasgow. It was felt that this theme should be brought to a wider audience in the form of a book of photographs, which outlines the main phases of Dreadnought construction.

I should like to thank Dr Chris Howard Bailey and Campbell McMurray, Director of the Royal Naval Museum, for their encouragement of and support for this project and for their advice on the content of the book. I would also like to record my thanks to the librarians who have aided my search for appropriate images, in particular to Deborah Potter, Curator of Photographs at the Royal Naval Museum, to Kate Hutcheson, manager of the Business Record Centre, University of Glasgow, for her enthusiasm and interest in this project, to Michael Moss, Archivist, University of Glasgow, for his support of this project and for allowing me use of the magnificent photographs from his collection, to Allan King of the Local History and Naval Collection, Portsmouth Central Library, for his patience over the years with my incursions on Dreadnoughts, and to Emma Chaplin, collections manager, The Dock Museum, Barrow-in-Furness, for quickly responding to my inquiries and interest in the Vickers Shipbuilding and Engineering Ltd photographic slide collection. Thanks also go to Betty Owen and David Clarke for meticulously reading the text in its formative phase. I should like to express my gratitude to Brian Patterson of the Portsmouth Dockyard Historic Trust for revealing, over several years, some of his invaluable knowledge of the workings of

Portsmouth Dockyard. Thanks are due also to Sue Goodger and Michael Forder, who also compiled the index. Lastly, my thanks go to Jonathan Falconer of Sutton Publishing for his patience when I was struggling to assemble the text and images.

For photographic images, thanks are due to Vickers Shipbuilding and Engineering Ltd, Barrow-in-Furness; the Dock Museum, Barrow-in-Furness; Business Records Centre, University of Glasgow; The Royal Naval Museum Photographic Collection; The Naval History Collection, Portsmouth City Library; and Portsmouth Royal Dockyard Historic Trust.

Roger D. Thomas
1998

INTRODUCTION:

Photographic Images as Representational Documents

The process of building the hull of HMS *Dreadnought* at Portsmouth Dockyard (1905–6) was carefully recorded in a series of regular photographic images. In the first week, two daily photographs were taken; after this, pictures were generally taken on a weekly basis. In all there are forty-eight distinct images of *Dreadnought*'s hull. After the launch the Admiralty became reticent over granting permission for photographs to be taken of the fitting-out of *Dreadnought*, so only a few images have survived. Subsequently, a limited number of photographs were taken of the hull construction of the other eight Dreadnoughts built at Portsmouth. The photographs of Dreadnought construction in Devonport Dockyard appear to have been lost in the dockyard fires of the Second World War. The National Maritime collection has just sixty-one surviving prints, and images of fitting-out are virtually unknown. The extraordinary concentration on the first Dreadnought partly hides the dearth of photographic material on the construction in the Royal Dockyards of later and more powerful warships. However, the Portsmouth-based photographers Silk and Cribb were able to take photographs of Dreadnought launches, with the notable exception of HMS *Royal Sovereign*, where only one image has survived.

On a comparative basis, the Royal Dockyard photographic holdings, with the exception of the launches, are unremarkable when compared with the imagery commissioned by John Brown, Clydebank. More than a thousand photographs have survived of the building of HMSs *Tiger*, *Barham*, *Repulse* and *Hood*. This is by far the largest photographic collection of this type of image in the United Kingdom. Records from the other major Dreadnought constructors are disappointing. Photographs from Sir W.G. Armstrong Whitworth and Palmers are now extremely rare. A few images can be found in contemporary naval journals.

Precisely what survives from Vickers, Barrow-in-Furness, remains something of a mystery, which will only be resolved when the surviving glass negatives are catalogued. At the moment, no images have been found of the building slip and only one of the fitting-out basin. The surviving national perspective remains highly dependent on the records of the Scottish yards, principally John Brown, Clydebank, for ship construction; and Beardmore, Dalmuir and Parkhead for workshops for machinery and armaments.

Few biographical details are known of the photographers who undertook this work. There are no local studies of the Portsmouth-based photographers Silk and Cribb, who also recorded many urban scenes in Portsmouth, so it is difficult to estimate how extensive their naval repertoire was. In these circumstances the John Brown commemorative albums are exceptional, because they contain a complete run of the different phases of Dreadnought construction and are especially significant with regard to the fitting-out phase. The photographers employed by this company tended to take pictures from three or four set positions, usually from cranes at the berth or the dockside. Their images are somewhat repetitious, although the pictures associated with HMS *Repulse* have a strong emphasis on recording the presence of shipyard workers. By way of contrast, Admiralty photographs hardly ever contain scenes of workmen. The Clydebank images also give a much better indication of the number of work gangs on a particular ship. The clarity of the detail allows the viewer to appreciate patterns and techniques of labour in much greater detail than do the narratives of contemporary books on naval architecture. However, even these fine collections have certain omissions, for there are no images of the assembly of the machinery in the boiler and engine rooms, or the interiors of turrets. Nor are there photographs of the fitting out of mess decks or officers' quarters. In the later phases of construction the ship was frequently profiled in an effort to elevate the Dreadnought's fine lines. Particularized details are sacrificed for an overall vista. These images seek to represent the omnipotence of the warship, which had both functional and aesthetic charac-teristics.

ABBREVIATIONS

The following abbreviations are used in the picture credits.

BRCUG   Business Records Centre, University of Glasgow

DNC   Director of Naval Construction

PCL   Portsmouth Central Library

PRDHT   Portsmouth Royal Dockyard Historical Trust

RNM   Royal Naval Museum

VSEL   Vickers Shipbuilding and Engineering Ltd

1: THE DREADNOUGHT PROGRAMME

The Programme

The laying of the first Dreadnought's keel plate on 2 October 1905 at the no. 5 building slip of Portsmouth Dockyard initiated the most concentrated programme of capital ship construction ever undertaken by the Royal Navy. When Dreadnought building ended in 1920, approximately £151 million had been spent on 35 battleships and 13 battle-cruisers. The original technical specification had been innovative – a turbine-driven battleship producing 23,000 s.h.p. for 21 knots, with a 10×12 inch main armament and a normal displacement of 18,120 tons. The programme ended with the successful sea trials of HMS *Hood*, a 42,600 ton battle-cruiser that achieved 32 knots at 144,000 s.h.p. and carried a heavy armament of 8×15 inch guns. After the First World War the Dreadnought programme lingered on in the Admiralty's 1920 drawings for a new class of 48,000 ton battle-cruisers with 9×16 inch guns and a class of 48,500 ton battleships with 9×18 inch guns. The provisional estimate for each of these ships was £7 million compared with the £1,785,68 for HMS *Dreadnought*.

Throughout the 1900s the two power standard as expressed in the numbers of British capital ships remained a political orthodoxy within Royal Naval circles, despite the reservations expressed between 1910 and 1912 by some Sea Lords about the nation's ability to sustain such high levels of naval expenditure. Some highly secret efforts were also made at the Admiralty to rethink naval strategy in 1913 in response to debates over the role of submarines and the financial anxieties of the Treasury. However, the tentative conclusions of these discussions were never released to the majority of cabinet members in the Liberal government and Dreadnoughts remained at the fore until the U-boat challenge of 1917–18.

The annual parliamentary naval vote for several years created Dreadnought classes of three ships, until 1909–10, when four Orion class battleships were ordered, a practice that continued with the subsequent King George V class in 1911, and the Iron Duke class in 1912. Between 1912 and 1913, five Queen Elizabeth class warships were laid down, followed in 1913 and 1914 by orders for five Royal Sovereigns. The private warship constructors finally built 34 battleships and battle-cruisers between February 1906 and 1920, while 17 Dreadnoughts were built in the Royal Dockyards. The Admiralty organized a system of competitive tendering from an approved list of private warship builders. Only companies that fulfilled stringent technical, organizational and management standards were listed. The Admiralty thought that management methods and the kind of supervision and control undertaken at particular shipyards directly affected the quality of work that could be expected from these firms. Initially, four companies made bids for Dreadnought contracts: Sir W.G. Armstrong Whitworth and Co. Ltd, John Brown and Co. Ltd, Fairfield Shipbuilding and Engineering Co. Ltd and Vickers Ltd. W. Beardmore and Co. Ltd and Scotts Shipbuilding and Engineering Ltd made representations to be included on the list in 1906. In all, ten firms were eventually given Dreadnought contracts: Armstrong Whitworth, which built 7 Dreadnoughts; Vickers, 6 Dreadnoughts; John Brown, 6

HMS *Valiant*, Queen Elizabeth class battleship, after the First World War, firing a broadside. (RNM Collection, 260/85(8))

Dreadnoughts; Fairfield, 4 Dreadnoughts; W. Beardmore, 3 Dreadnoughts; Palmers Shipbuilding and Iron Co. Ltd, 3 Dreadnoughts; Scotts, 2 Dreadnoughts; Cammell Laird and Co. Ltd, 1 Dreadnought; Thames Iron Works, 1 Dreadnought; and Harland and Wolff Ltd, 1 Dreadnought. Armstrong Whitworth's figures included two battleships initially contracted for foreign powers. *Rio de Janeiro* was built for the Brazilian government (1911–12) and was then transferred to the Ottoman government as *Sultan Osman I* (9 January 1914), before being taken by the British government as HMS *Agincourt*. The ship joined the Grand Fleet on 26 August 1914. HMS *Canada* was built for the Chilean government (1911–14; *Almirante Latorre*) and was purchased by the British government on 9 September 1914. Similarly, Vickers built *Reshadieh* for the Imperial Ottoman government (1912–14). The ship was then acquired for the British battle fleet as HMS *Erin* in August 1914.

Building Costs

It has been suggested that prominent commercial firms estimated the dockyards' pricing system and labour charges and then integrated these figures with their own costings for armoured plate, armaments, turbines, auxiliary engines and boilers. They then submitted lower bids than the dockyards. However, the actual costs of Dreadnoughts remained uneven. For instance, the Devonport-built battle-cruiser *Indefatigable* (1909–11) was £220,000 cheaper than the price for *New Zealand*, built by Fairfield (1910–12). In the majority of cases, however, the private shipyards were cheaper than the Royal Dockyards. With the Bellerophon class (1906–09), Armstrong Whitworth was cheaper by £74,615, and Vickers cheaper by £123,866 with the St Vincent class (1907–10). Cheaper builds of around £35,000 were completed by W. Beardmore, Armstrong Whitworth and Thames Iron Works for the Orion class (1909–12) and, with respect to the King George V class (1911–13), lower construction costs were achieved at Scotts and Cammell Laird. Nevertheless, respective dockyard and shipyard costs for the Lion class (1909–13) were remarkably similar, and those of the Queen Elizabeth class (1912–16) mixed: *Queen Elizabeth*, Portsmouth Dockyard, £3,014,103; *Malaya*, Armstrong Whitworth, £2,945,709; *Valiant*, Fairfield, £2,537,037; *Warspite*, Devonport Dockyard, £2,524,148; and *Barham*, John Brown, £2,470,113. Costings were a complicated matter because methods of manning and squadding were different between the dockyards, which used the special category of skilled labourers, and the private yards, where plating, riveting and caulking were listed trades. It was actually quite difficult for contemporaries to produce direct comparisons between the Royal Dockyards and the private yards in terms of cost, efficiency and productivity.

The Admiralty remained rigorous over Dreadnought tendering because of the excessive profits made by some contractors, principally Fairfield, on cruiser contracts during the 1890s. It was noticed in 1902–3 that this firm had paid a 20 per cent dividend to its shareholders, which rose to

30 per cent in 1905–6. However, in the changed circumstances of the depression of 1909–10, John Brown, Clydebank, made a loss on the £312,950 contract for the cruiser HMS *Bristol*. The Admiralty usually allowed reasonable profit margins on Dreadnought contracts because of its awareness of the large capital sums invested in plant and machinery, and of the necessity for the firms on its list to remain profitable while maintaining a regular flow of capital ships.

Rates of Construction

The building of HMS *Dreadnought* at Portsmouth Dockyard in twelve months (2 October 1905–3 October 1906) was a prestigious exercise and unrepresentative of subsequent construction work in the Royal Dockyards. Much of the material had been pre-assembled and work was well advanced in the mould loft when the keel plate was laid. The 12 inch guns and the hydraulic machinery had been ordered in January 1905, the main propelling machinery on 24 June, and the armour and principal ship castings in August. Large amounts of overtime were paid to the dockyard workers, who worked a 69 hour week and not their usual 48 hour week. Work started at 6.00 a.m. rather than the usual 7.00 a.m. and finished at 6.00 p.m. instead of 5.00 p.m. The lunch hour was reduced to 30 minutes. A six day week was also introduced. Some workers were even instructed to continue working on Christmas Day and New Year's Day. During the early construction work, 1,100 men were employed, although this was subsequently increased to 3,000. It took

just eighteen weeks from the laying of the keel plates to the launch on 10 February 1906. The ship was commissioned on 1 September. The preliminary hydraulic trials were completed on 12 and 13 September, the official steam trials were held on 1 October 1906, and the torpedo and gunnery trials were on 16 October. All trials were completed by 22 October. HMS *Dreadnought* was built two months ahead of schedule. The remarkable rapidity of the construction was intended to influence German naval observers and to exaggerate the speed of construction that could be attained in British yards.

The second Portsmouth-built Dreadnought, HMS *Bellerophon*, took 27 months to build. This was still quicker than the earlier Portsmouth battleship average of 31 months. Construction times in the private yards were longer still: 39 months for the Lord Nelson class (1905–8), Beardmore and Palmers; and 33 months for the King Edward VII class (1902–5), Fairfield, John Brown and Vickers. The later construction schedules remained similar to those of HMS *Bellerophon*. HMS *Queen Elizabeth* was built in 27 months at Portsmouth Dockyard and HMS *Warspite* in 28 months at Devonport, while HMSs *Royal Oak* and *Royal Sovereign* were completed in 27 months. This was a similar length of time to that taken by Vickers, Barrow-in-Furness, in building HMS *Revenge*, but quicker than Palmers, Jarrow, for HMS *Resolution*. Beardmore, Dalmuir, took 42 months to complete HMS *Ramillies*, but this was because of damage sustained at the launch. Private

HMS *Queen Elizabeth* in foreground with Orion-class battleships in background, *c*. 1915. (RNM Collection, 987/82)

yards could certainly achieve rapid construction times, as with *Vanguard*, Vickers, which took 22 months, and most impressively with the battle-cruisers HMS *Renown* at Fairfield, Glasgow, and HMS *Repulse* at John Brown, Clydebank, which were completed in 20 months and 19 months respectively. The final Dreadnought, HMS *Hood*, Clydebank, took 42 months to complete, although several delays were caused through changes in the ship's specification and the uncertainty over the future of the class.

Dreadnought Designs

Although the Director of Naval Construction (DNC) at the Admiralty had the final word, the design was usually the work of a small team of naval architects, whose members were allowed some specialization. Among the more well-known naval constructors associated with the design of Dreadnoughts were J.H. Narbeth, (HMS *Dreadnought*, Invincible class, Bellerophon class), W.H. Whiting (Invincible class), W.T. Davis (Indefatigable class, Lion class), E.N. Mooney and A.M. Worthington (HMS

Neptune, Orion class, King George V class, Iron Duke class), E.L. Attwood (Lion class, HMS *Tiger*, Renown class, HMS *Hood*), E.N. Mooney and W.H. Gard (Queen Elizabeth class), W.H. Gard and W. Berry (Renown class) and S.V. Goodall (Glorious class, HMS *Furious*, HMS *Hood*).

The two DNCs who were strongly associated with the Dreadnought project, Philip Watts (1902–12) and Eustace d'Eyncourt (1912 onwards), had both spent many years working in private industry before taking up their Admiralty appointment. Watts had completed a shipwright apprenticeship at Portsmouth Dockyard, where he won an Admiralty scholarship to the School of Naval Architecture at South Kensington, London. He worked at Pembroke Dockyard before moving on to the Admiralty, where he was allocated to the calculating section. He had spells at Pembroke Dockyard and Chatham Dockyard before moving, in 1885, at the age of thirty-nine, to occupy the position of technical director at Armstrong Whitworth, Elswick site, a post formerly held by the then current DNC, Sir William White. On the latter's retirement through ill health, Watts was appointed DNC in 1902.

Eustace d'Eyncourt went to Charterhouse and then trained as a Naval architect at Armstrong Whitworth, where he worked in the design office under Perrett. He was sent to Greenwich Naval College as a private student by Watts, then director of Armstrong Whitworth. D'Eyncourt completed his apprenticeship in 1891 and moved to Fairfield in 1899, where he became technical director. Following Watts's appointment to DNC, Perrett invited d'Eyncourt to return to Armstrong Whitworth as chief of design. He was subsequently appointed DNC in 1912, with the support of Winston Churchill, First Lord of the Admiralty. Watts stayed on for a year in an advisory capacity, possibly because d'Eyncourt had no dockyard experience.

Ship design was the only portion of warship construction that was completely worked out at the Admiralty. The designs and working drawings for gun mountings, guns and machinery were undertaken by the main contractors. According to d'Eyncourt, a ship's brief was initially discussed at the Board of Admiralty, and the Board's decisions were then conveyed by the Controller to the DNC for him to complete a preliminary design. The DNC then worked on the ship's main features in terms of the hull, its length, breadth and draught; the hull's appropriateness to current docking facilities; the ship's armaments and propulsion, in particular the s.h.p.; and the desired speeds at varying degrees of load. A model was then run, usually at the Haslar experimental tank, to obtain more reliable figures. More detailed plans were then made of the arrangement of the ship's armour, boiler rooms and machinery space. The sketched design, showing all of the appropriate figures, the final legend and weights, was then submitted to the Admiralty Board for confirmation. Once this had been given, the full specification of the ship was worked out in relation to the hull compartments, decks, engines, boilers and auxiliary engines and the storage of fuel, ammunition, water, stores and provisions. When this work was completed, the Admiralty Board again approved the specifications and plans, and the official stamp was placed on the sheer drawings and the midships sections.

On HMS *Dreadnought* the plans initially included the sheer draught, mid sections, profile, bridge deck, flying deck and forecastle, upper deck, main deck, lower deck, platform and hold, sections fore and aft, and armour drawings. DNC Watts initially deployed a team of two assistant constructors and five draughtsmen to work on these drawings. Three more draughtsmen worked on engineering lithos, the coaling arrangements, storage and magazines, the shell rooms, the torpedo rooms, the disposition of small guns and ammunition, boat storage, the details of the masts, the control position, and the auxiliary machinery rooms and ventilation. Individual assistant constructors were also given their own briefs: Ballantyne worked on the ship's stability and metacentre, while Payne and Attwood worked on the ship's coaling, water and oil capacity. The team was steadily added to until it peaked at three assistant controllers and thirteen draughtsmen. In 1909, DNC Philip Watts informed the Admiralty Board that the specification and documents that formed the basis of a battleship contract of the Orion class hull had reached 269 pages, whereas 130 pages had been sufficient for a new battleship in 1899. These increased demands led to larger teams. A DNC letter of 15 January 1912 recorded that 24 draughtsmen were to be allocated to the Iron Duke project for a period of two years. The Queen Elizabeth class initially required 28 draughtsmen, while a further 40 were employed for 3 hours overtime each day. In all, 50 draughtsmen signed the Admiralty's security document for this class of battleship.

The Plans

Dreadnought design plans were dispatched from the Admiralty by couriers to the dockyards and shipyards contracted to build the ships. Initially a single copy was taken, and the original plans returned to the Admiralty. The draughtsmen subsequently made duplicate copies, usually four prints. The plans that were exchanged usually included those of the lines, profile, shelter deck, flying deck, upper deck, main deck, middle deck, lower deck, platforms, hold, section forward and section aft, but copies were also made of the plans that related to the arrangement of the armour, the machinery in the engine room and the boiler room, and the location of auxiliary machinery and workshop spaces. The number of copies and the length of time for which they could be retained varied from ship to ship. For example, five sets of the Orion plans were returned from Portsmouth Dockyard to the Admiralty on 1 November 1909, but eleven further sets were then sent to Portsmouth Dockyard from Palmers, Scotts and Vickers, which had all unsuccessfully tendered for the Orion class. A major

HMS *Valiant* in the North Sea, *c.* 1918, showing war modifications of searchlight towers around the after funnel, flying off positions on 'B' and 'X' turrets and extra tops to the tripod and main mast. (RNM Collection, 127/81)

reorganization of administrative practices appears to have occurred with the King George V class, because the bulk of the copies of the plans were made at Portsmouth Dockyard and Devonport Dockyard. This practice was continued for the Iron Duke class. Although Beardmore had won the contract for HMS *Benbow* and Vickers for the *Emperor of India*, these firms were left with a minimal amount of work, which was restricted to boat storage, messing and sleeping arrangements, galleys and sky lights.

Work in the Mould Loft
Mould lofts varied considerably in size. At John Brown, Clydebank, the room measured 376 × 53 ft, the proportions at Beardmore, Dalmuir, were 300 × 70 ft, while at Portsmouth Dockyard the mould

loft, built in 1893 and enlarged in 1908, measured 150 × 100 ft. In general the lofts had yellow pine floors, since this wood made the best scrive boards because they did not tear under the scrive knife. The planking was tongued and grooved at the edges and the screws were sunk beneath floor level. The holes were filled in with dowels. The floor was planed afresh after each ship had been layed off. The basic tools employed in the mould loft were a banjo frame for transferring curves, trammels, compasses, T-squares, measuring staffs, steel tape, quadrants, tracing paper and floor dusters. A small workshop was located nearby. This contained circular and band saws, planes and planing machines, carpenter's benches and trestle tables. A large mat was kept at the entrance to keep out dust.

While the process of recall, tracing and storage of the ship's plans was under way, the plans of the sheer draught, the decks and sections were assembled in the mould lofts of the respective yards. The loftsmen were also responsible for the selective ordering of customized plate and castings. An important aspect of the work related to 'laying off' the sheer draught, which consisted of three plans: the sheer plan, the half-breadth plan and the body plan. It was the sheer plan that showed the frame stations and bulkheads throughout a Dreadnought. It also revealed the form of the Dreadnought's hull at the centre line. The half-breadth plan showed the margin line, the water lines from stem to stern and the beam-end lines. The body plan was copied full size on the mould loft floor by means of a system of dots and chalked lines. It demonstrated the lines of each transverse frame at a given station and outlined the form of the hull at each displacement station. The full-size body plan was also the principal guide to the profile of the various frames. The frame stations and individual frames were coded, and these numbers were subsequently painted onto each frame. After the points of the lines had been drawn on the floor, a light batten secured by pins was superimposed onto the chalk profile. The lines were then cut into the scrive boards (the floor).

In the Royal Dockyards the loftsmen were shipwrights, and they were assisted by small numbers of apprentices. The work was regarded as varied and mentally stimulating – 'a gentleman's life' compared with the more exposed work on the uncovered slip. Loftsmen's work required a considerable amount of individual skill and cooperative teamwork. Although craftsmen and semi-skilled labourers had evolved an experiential knowledge of the broad processes of ship construction, this could not hide their dependency on the technical work carried out by the loftsmen.

Models

The most well-known models were associated with the work of R.E. Froude at Haslar, where several models of the first Dreadnought's hull were used in the water tank to analyse and fine the dimensions of the ship's lines and beam. In all, seven models were made. HMS *Dreadnought*'s cover book reveals a complex correspondence between DNC Watts, assistant constructor Narbeth and R.E. Froude through February and March 1905 over displacement, filling out the ship's bow, the shape of the propellers and the location of the inward propeller shafts. Five basic hull shapes were subsequently used for ten classes of Dreadnought. The major function of the wax models that were made of Dreadnought hulls was to obtain a complete presentation of the shell plating. The frames, strakes, keelsons and side stringers were all drawn on the model, while the length of each plate and its breadth at each end were measured from the model. The measurements ordered from the model and scrive boards for plates had sufficient margins to allow for later adjustment: A. Campbell Holms (*Practical Shipbuilding* vol. 1, 1918) recorded that

7 per cent wastage on the plate was a low figure, while 11 per cent was considered to be high.

A different model from the above was that of a completed ship. There was a considerable correspondence in 1913 between the management of Armstrong Whitworth and the Admiralty over the form of the model for HMS *Malaya*. This had been requested by the Malay States, which were funding the cost of the battleship. The choice was between a ⅛ inch to 1 ft model at £1,000 or an ¼ inch to 1 ft model at £1,700. The Admiralty decided on the larger scale, although the Armstrong Whitworth management insisted that this price did not include packing, insurance, freight and delivery. The model was dispatched in a glass-sided mahogany case on 25 August 1913. HMS *Malaya* was completed in February 1916. One of the largest ship models to have survived from the Dreadnought era was made of HMS *Warspite* by trainee shipwrights at Devonport Dockyard.

Moulds

Moulds were made for the keel blocks and plates. Special moulds were manufactured for the shaft brackets, while others related to the watertight and oiltight frames, to the stem and stern castings, and to the accompanying cradle moulds for contour plates. N.J. McDermaid (*Shipyard Practice as Applied to Warship Construction*, 1911) states that two basic techniques were used for preparing armour plates: laying off, which was used for the middle portions of the hull, and mocking up, which was used for the ends of the hull. Several moulds were made for each plate: two sections with outwinders, two planes with outsiders, and one surface mould. Individual moulds also had to be made for the rudders.

Plate

The armoured plate used in Dreadnought construction was subject to competitive tendering from an Admiralty-approved list of companies. It was administered by the director of contracts, who laid down the specific requirements for mild steel; nickel-steel plates, which were used for the decks and protective bulkheads; high-tension steel plates, which were used for the upper deck; and armoured plate. The bulk of the armoured plate was obtained from Vickers, the River Don Works, Sheffield; Armstrong Whitworth, Elswick; Beardmore, Parkhead; John Brown, the Atlas Works, Sheffield; and Cammell Laird, the Cyclops Works, Sheffield. Individual firms often obtained the contract for several ships in the same class. Vickers had the contract for the main belt armour on HMS *Queen Elizabeth* and HMS *Warspite*. Special Admiralty inspection officers were appointed to evaluate the plate at the steel mills, as with the case of the overseer, F.E. Coast of Janson Street, Sheffield, who was instructed to inspect the armoured plate manufactured at the River Don Works for the Queen Elizabeth class. Special steel plates were also obtained for these ships from Messrs Spencer, Colville, the Steel Company, Scotland, while Hadfield Steel Ltd of the Hecla Works, Sheffield, received contracts for the conning tower roof and the armouring of the rangefinders.

After the plate had been rolled, it was sent by rail and sea to the on-site plate shops at the yards, where it had to be stacked, or bent using hydraulic bending machines. Light plate shopwork involved drilling, shearing, planing, flanging and bevelling. Much of this could be achieved using specialist machines. In 1909, Fairfield Shipyard had 20 punching and shearing machines, 7 rollers, 5 planers and 7 beam machines. In the Dreadnought era, many specialist companies manufactured shipbuilding machine tools and plate and section working tools. The journal *Jane's Fighting Ships* usually carried the advertisements of James Bennie and Sons, Glasgow; Craig and Donald, St Johnstone; Hugh Smith and Sons, Glasgow; Sir W.G. Armstrong, Whitworth and Co., Manchester; Platt and Field, Manchester;

F. Berry and Sons, Sowerby; Scriven and Co., Leeds; and Greenwood and Batley, Leeds. Admiralty orders for mild steel plates of 10 to 40 lb[1] were usually set at 4,000 to 5,000 tons; those for nickel steel plates of 20 lb, 30 lb, 40 lb and 50 lb were set at 1,000 tons, as in the case of the HMS *Orion* orders of 8 July 1909. *Orion's* specialized 60 lb tapered plate was ordered in much smaller quantities, 200 tons being deemed sufficient, and 50 tons of nickel steel rivets were also ordered. The Admiralty kept to three or four established suppliers, as can be seen from the letter from the Director of Construction of 26 June 1912, which invited bids for special steel plates similar to those supplied to the *Iron Duke's* control director (1571–1911) from Messrs Spencer, plate numbers 391 from Beardmore, and unannealled and annealled plates similar to numbers 770 and 1812 on the 1911 list from Colville.

1. In shipbuilding, plate thicknesses are represented as pounds weight per square foot; 10 lb equals a ¼ of an inch thickness.

2: PREPARATORY WORK

The early manual work was concerned with the preparation of bars and frames in the heavy and light plate shops. The initial markings for the bars were obtained from the lines cut in the scrive boards. A separate frame list was also used to describe the details of each frame. A variety of bars were used on Dreadnoughts. These included angle bars, which were deployed to join plates and stiffen bulkheads and frames. They were also used with beams and carlings for the decks. Z bars were associated with beams in the platform decks. They were also used to obtain stiffening, to support bulkheads and for the framing of the ends of the hull. Channel bars were also commonly used in stiffening. T bars were restricted to masts, H and I bars were associated with watertight bulkheads, and segmental bars were used to finish the top edges of hatches, ladder ways and the coffer dams in the boiler rooms. Efforts to mechanize this preparatory work were limited. Frame angles had to be heated uniformly in furnaces and, since the shell flange stretched at the bilge when it was bent after being heated, the marking of the rivet holes were laid down to an Admiralty formula, depending on the type of work to be done. Bar and frame bending was undertaken on steel slabs, usually 12–15 yd in length and 40 yd in width. The depth was about 1 ft. The slab was perforated by large holes 1.5 inches in diameter and 6 inches apart, which took the steel plugs around which the hot frames were bent. The angle smiths used a set iron initially and fixed it into the slab using wedges and plugs. The heated frames were then taken from the furnace, fixed at one end and bent to profile to fit the set iron. The frame was hammered into shape especially on the edges if it did not fit the scrive board measurements. Once the top fitted the floor, head and bevel lines were marked on it. The shape of the frame with its marking was then drawn on the slab. The set was then reversed and the appropriate outline again drawn on the slab. The frame angle was heated up and then bent to the shape of the set using levers and iron bars to force the appropriate fit. The dogs then fixed it in position. The cooled frames were then checked against the scrive measurements. Further hammering or bending occurred if the alignment was inaccurate.

Armaments

Heavy naval armament was dominated by two firms: Armstrong Whitworth at Elswick and Vickers at the River Don Works, Sheffield, and Barrow-in-Furness. Their rival, Coventry Ordnance, was based on three firms (John Brown, Cammell Laird and Fairfield); they did not succeed in substantively breaking into the British capital ship market before the First World War. The Liberal government elected in 1906 was particularly concerned in its early years to obtain a reduction in armament expenditure. Consequently the Admiralty had to argue in 1908 that battleship construction was needed to prevent the heavy armaments industry from coming to a standstill. It stated that the absence of orders would close down armoured plate production and the erection of gun turrets would also cease. There was some overcapacity in the industry during these years and this created serious problems for Beardmore, which had built new naval gun shops at Parkhead. Although these works were operative in 1909, the firm was only able to obtain heavy gun orders for its own ship, HMS *Ramillies*. Heavy gun barrels had to be forged, hammered, wired, bored, rifled and inspected. The lathes used in this work were among the largest of the machines utilized in heavy engineering. Specialist firms like Alfred Herbert Ltd of Coventry supplied this market. The completed gun barrels were transported by rail to the dockyards and shipyards.

particular at Hadfield Projectiles, Sheffield, which was at this time the largest shell manufacturer in the world. During the First World War, heavy shell production was greatly increased in the shell shops at Barrow-in-Furness, Elswick and Parkhead. Much of the labour force in the shell shops was diluted during the war under the terms of the 1907 Munitions Act. The machine work was generally undertaken by women operatives. Vickers had redeployed selected skilled machinists from their gun shops to the shell shops where they established the rates and charts for a premium bonus system, a method of piece-rate payment that had been recognized by the Amalgamated Society of Engineers (ASE) in the 1902 Carlisle agreement. The Vickers management promoted handymen from the shell shop to gun work in an effort to reduce wages. There was also a sustained effort to introduce more apprentices in place of handymen. These policies brought them into conflict in 1905, 1908, 1911 and 1917 with their skilled workers, who were supported by the ASE. J.T. Murphy, who worked at Vickers, Brightside, turning propeller shafts and gun barrels, came to national prominence when he wrote the pamphlet 'The workers' committee: an outline of its principles and structure' in 1917. Similar disputes occurred at Armstrong Whitworth and on the Clyde, for the workshop movement was part of a national campaign against dilution and industrial conscription.

Shell Manufacture

The 12, 13.5 and 15 inch shells for the heavy guns were made at specialist firms, in

Marine Engineering

The most modern engine and boiler shops that had the capacity to manufacture machinery for Dreadnoughts were built at Dalmuir by Beardmore. They covered 5.5 acres and were equipped with the latest machinery, which was powered individually rather than by the older band- or shaft-driven techniques. Despite the new plant the firm was unable to obtain substantial naval contracts until 1910. The turbines used for Dreadnoughts were manufactured by Parsons, and Brown and Curtis. The battle-cruiser HMS *Tiger* (June 1912 – October 1914) was the first ship to have Brown and Curtis turbines. These were built under licence by John Brown, Clydebank. They were heavier than Parsons and were used for HMSs *Repulse, Renown, Courageous, Furious* and *Hood.* Several specialist firms, including Thos. Firth and Sons Ltd, Sheffield, obtained contracts for turbine components, while the Darlington Forge Company placed adverts in *Jane's Fighting Ships* (1916 and 1918), showing images of forged ingot steel turbine rotor drums, rotor wheels and spindles. The Admiralty awarded turbine contracts on dockyard Dreadnoughts to Scotts, Harland and Wolff, Wallsend Slipway, Hawthorn Leslie and Cammell Laird. Boiler making was dominated by two firms: Babcock and Wilcox (20 Dreadnoughts) and Yarrows (16 Dreadnoughts). Some were built under licence, as with Harland and Wolff (HMS *Neptune*) and John Brown (HMS *Barham*). Small tube boilers were adopted for HMSs *Courageous, Glorious, Furious* and *Hood.*

During the First World War, Armstrong Whitworth installed automatic machinery in its Elswick marine workshops and increasingly introduced women workers, who undertook forms of repetitious production involving light components and the preparatory work in the electrical and turbine shops. Large numbers of women were also recruited by Beardmore, Fairfield and Portsmouth Dockyard for similar work. There were campaigns against the Munitions Act in the engineering and marine workshops in the Clyde region between 1915 and 1918 over the length of the working day – the demand was for a 40 hour week – and various forms of dilution. The shop steward committees were especially militant during 1917, although their campaigns did not spread to the Boilermakers' Society (the United Society of Boilermakers and Iron and Steel Shipbuilders; USBISS) and the Shipwrights' and Shipconstructors' Association (SSA). The Clyde Workers' Committee received support at several marine engineering works, principally Dalmuir and Parkhead, where the Independent Labour Party (ILP) socialist Kirkwood had enforced a closed shop. Other Scottish firms that had shop steward committees included the Babcock and Wilcox factory at Renfrew and Weir's factory at Cathcart, which specialized in naval hydraulic systems, condensers, circulating pumps and fuel pumps. The Barr and Stroud works at Scotstoun, which made rangefinders and naval optical equipment, also had active works committees.

The mould loft at Beardmore, Dalmuir. The room measured 300 × 70 ft. The building was erected by Sir William Arrol and Co. Ltd, Glasgow. (BRCUG)

The mould loft at John Brown, Clydebank. The room measured 376 × 53 ft. (BRCUG)

The shipyard drawing office at Beardmore, Dalmuir. Draughtsmen were recruited by examination from craftsmen of the Construction, Mechanical and Electrical Departments of the shipbuilding industry. Completed drawings were sent to the Tracing Section, which was generally staffed by women. (BRCUG)

Rolling mill, John Brown, Atlas Works, Sheffield. The plant for manufacturing armour plate was of special construction that was not adaptable to ordinary commercial work. Because of the high content of nickel and chromium used in making armour plate, exceptionally high temperatures had to be achieved in the furnaces. Ingots of 80–100 tons were used in the specially designed melting furnaces. The forging was carried out by 10,000–12,000 ton hydraulic presses. The slab was then reheated and was rolled in an exceptionally powerful mill, which was able to deal with plates of up to 15 ft in width and 50 ft in length. After the heat treatment in the furnaces, the plate was straightened under a heavy hydraulic press. A large planing machine was then used to bring it to the required thickness. (BRCUG)

Rolling armour plate, Parkhead, Glasgow. In 1904 Beardmore purchased a licence from Harvey United Steel Co., USA, to manufacture Krupps and Harvey armour plate. The profits made from the armour plate and steel production sustained Beardmore through the heavy losses of 1906–10, when the newly built naval yard at Dalmuir (completed in 1908) was unable to obtain substantial naval contracts. The annual capacity of Parkhead was 10,000 tons of armour plate, 50,000 tons of boiler and ship plate, and 60,000 tons of castings. The peak demand was in 1910, when 11,641 tons of armour plate were sold. Beardmore annually supplied *c.* 8,000 tons of armour plate to Vickers, Barrow-in-Furness, and Scotts, Greenock. Contemporary estimates in *Brassey's Naval and Shipping Annual* suggest that an annual production of 10,000 tons of armour plate involved capital costs of £1 million to £1.5 million. (BRCUG)

Bogie furnaces for carbonizing armour, John Brown, Atlas Works, Sheffield. The slab of armour plate was placed inside these special furnaces for two to three weeks, during which the carbon was adsorbed onto the face. (BRCUG)

The armour plate erection shop, Beardmore, Parkhead. Heavy overhead cranes were used to move the stacked plate. (BRCUG)

A Dreadnought's belt armour in the armour plate shop, John Brown, Clydebank. Planing machines for armour plate are at the end of the shop. (BRCUG)

Armour plate shop no. 5, Beardmore, Parkhead. (BRCUG)

Armour plate being bent by a 12,000 ton hydraulic press, Beardmore, Parkhead. (BRCUG)

Right: Steel ingot under a 10,000 ton hydraulic press. John Brown, Atlas Steel Works, Sheffield. (BRCUG)

Below: The general office and stacks of steel plate, John Brown, Clydebank. (BRCUG)

Members of the Boilermakers' Society bending frames in the plate shop at Beardmore, Dalmuir. The work was undertaken on steel slabs, which were perforated by large holes 1.5 inches in diameter and 6 inches in depth. These received the steel plugs around which the hot frames were bent. Angle ironsmiths furnaced the frames, and the platers took the frames and bent them into the appropriate

profiles. The same bending techniques were used for frames, beams and bars. This type of work was not mechanized because of the large number of variations in the profiles of the frames and beams used in the construction of Dreadnoughts. (BRCUG)

3: The Building Slip

Laying the Keel Plate and Early Framing
On the slipway early preparatory work was the erection and alignment of building blocks on which the ship would be built. In the Royal Dockyards, five metal derricks were usually placed on either side of the hull to lift the heavier plate, which could weigh up to 8 tons, and prefabricated sections, 10 tons. In the private shipyards the capital investment in this equipment was significantly greater. In 1914 the Vickers' yard at Barrow used nine Arrol tower cranes across four berths. These had a 60 ft radius for weights of up to 10 tons and a 120 ft radius for 5 ton weights. At John Brown, Clydebank, and Fairfield, Govan, lattice masts and derrick systems were employed at the building slip. A more elaborate method was utilized by Beardmore at the naval yard, Dalmuir, where an Arrol metal gantry system had been erected over the two building berths. Additional mobile metal cranes were also used. Harland and Wolff, Belfast, had similarly installed an Arrol gantry, which was combined with hydraulic riveting, for the building of the liners RMS *Olympic* and RMS *Titanic* on slips 2 and 3, North Yard. Despite its prestigious construction

contracts, this yard only received one Dreadnought order: the battle-cruiser HMS *Glorious* (1915–17).

The laying of the keel plates on the slip floor was one the earliest acts of construction. In the dockyards this was the subject of a brief naval ceremony.

'It is correct that there is no fixed ceremony, the official birth of the ship being the launch . . . when it is done at this dockyard, the ceremony (the keel plate) consists of a 20 ft keel plate being slung and landed in the position in the presence of the lady who after seeing the level applied and verifying the position of the plate with reference to the middle line and exact position fore and aft declares the plate well and truly laid.'

Admiralty memorandum to
Japanese Inquiry, 1911

'The blocks were erected forward, amidships and aft to heights given in the drawings. Midway between these a base is erected, and its lower edge sighted in with the top of the existing blocks, and a set built up to this height. From these sets of blocks a series of four or five blocks is erected and trimmed by stretching a line along the upper surface, and sighting from end to end. For the complicated stern blocks, moulds would be made on the mould loft floor, and the blocks set up to the moulds.'

N.J. McDermaid, *Shipyard Practice As Applied to Warship Construction*, 1911

The next phases were concerned with the erection of the flat and vertical keels. Work then proceeded to the construction of the double bottom with its complex network of frames, longitudinals and beams. With the Queen Elizabeth class the transverse frames were situated at 4 ft sequences, both forward and aft of the double bottom. These frames were made up from channel and Z bars. The longitudinal strength was secured by the use of stringers, which were worked intercostally with the frames. They were situated midway between the decks. The transverse frames were riveted to floor plates and secured to the keel. They were bracketed to transverse beams. On HMS *Hood* the keel box construction developed for the Royal Sovereign class was adopted. It was continued over the length of the double bottom. Z bars were used to reinforce those sections that had to bear particularly heavy weights. The framing continued amidships and commenced with the riveting together of three component parts: a frame angle, a reverse bar and a floor plate. These together formed a single unit. Frame erection was undertaken at a rapid rate. The technical details of the keel and double bottom of the first Dreadnought are outlined in clear dia-grammatic form in J.M. Roberts' *The Battleship Dreadnought* (1992), which also contains comprehensive scale drawings of the side framing at midships, forward hull, aft hull, a profile of the outer bottom plating and the sequence of plates at the stem and stern.

Plating

The craftwork that was undertaken on the building slip involved a profuse number of small gangs of workers. In the private yards the erection of the hull was organized through a series of contracts negotiated between the management and the numerous trade gangs. These gangs recruited their own labour and supervised the work to be undertaken within each gang. In the dockyards this work was organized in a quite different manner. It was largely undertaken by a stratum referred to as skilled labourers who were paid time rates. They were not classified by the Admiralty as tradesmen, despite numerous petitions requesting their recognition as riveters or caulkers. Skilled labourers were moved from job to job in the yard and were usually supervised by shipwrights. These gangs had far less control on the job than the equivalent tradesmen in private yards. In the Clyde shipyards there were separate gangs composed of both skilled tradesmen and semi-skilled men. Here the role of the shipwright was more restricted. They were responsible for liaising with the mould loft and for setting the keel blocks and the preparations for the launch. They also checked the positioning and fairing of the frames and the large castings for the stem. Plating was the province of platers, who were organized into gangs of five or six men. They were paid at a fixed rate for the completion of a row of plates. They were responsible for organizing their helpers, who were paid on a time basis. Some platers worked with the templates provided from the mould loft; others undertook the punching of holes and the bending of the plate. The plates had to be lifted by the derricks or cranes as gangs moved along the puddocks to manhandle them into position on the berth. When the work progressed to the decks, greater care had to be taken over the lifting technique. The plates were pushed into position and then bolted down. Each member of the squad knew what the other members' work was about and had undertaken this in earlier gangs. The squads acquired 'on the job' knowledge gained across working lives of all of the necessary methods required for plating on the berth. A high degree of coordination was required in this kind of work. Little daily direct supervision was given outside the individual squad, although plates were regularly inspected for the quality of the fitting by charge hands and foremen. The key representatives of the company were the foremen, who were responsible for negotiating with the gangs of platers the piece rate. They also had to maintain the smooth progress of the work so that the firm met the dates of its contract schedule.

Riveting

Dreadnought hulls required millions of rivets, and these were put there by squads of workers. A typical riveter gang consisted of two riveters – one a left-handed striker and one a right-handed striker – a holder up and a heater, who was often a boy. The heater worked the small coke portable furnace and heated the rivets until they were white hot. He then tossed them to the holder up, who bumped them into the hole and held them there with a long hammer, known as a Dolly. In shell riveting the two hammermen were on the other side of the plate and they knocked the rivet down with alternate blows. Once the rivet was set firm and had cooled, a further sequence of blows rounded off its edge. A rivet could be hammered in in 1 minute when the squad was working flat out. This involved approximately fifteen strikes from each hitter. While several skills were required to achieve and sustain the precision and rhythm of the strikes, the riveters also had to cope with the monotony of the work, which was always exposed to the outside elements. In winter they had to cover their shirts with layers of cardigans or old jackets to keep out the wind and rain. The work was always tiring because of the required body stance. Long hours and fatigue combined to make it an arduous job. The strikers in particular preferred to work in short, intensive bursts and then to recuperate in longer recovery periods. The work was also often dangerous, with the men working high up on the puddocks on insecure deck plating. They were exposed to the hazards created by the full force of winter weather. There was a tendency for squads to keep together and to employ existing friends or relatives where possible.

A variety of rivets were required, depending on the nature of the work, the thickness of the plate and its location. Heavy hammers had to be used in keel riveting because of the length of the keel. Minor misalignments of holes were corrected by driving in tapered steel pins known as Drifts to enlarge the hole. When this was insufficient the hole was rimed by using a pneumatic power drill. Hand riveting remained predominant on Dreadnought hull construction, because hydraulic riveting machines had a limited role in the shipyards: they were usually used for the keel and beam riveting. They were not used in the Royal Dockyards for shell plating, although they were introduced at both Beardmore, Dalmuir, and John Brown, Clydebank. However, pneumatic rivet guns were widely adopted during the 1900s in both the dockyards and the shipyards. Because of the intervention of USBISS, full squads of riveters were employed whenever the guns were used, even though the work could technically have been done by an unskilled man.

Again a variety of rivets had to be used in the erection of the hull. The most common type was the pan head. Countersunk heads were utilized when a flush finish was required or in areas where structural strength and/or watertightness was required. Snap points were similar in role to hammered heads but were used in accommodation areas for an improved appearance. The countersunk rivets were used to join three thicknesses of plate. Tap rivets, which were threaded, were used to join plates to armour plate or to join plate to castings.

As with the squads of platers, the rivet gangs were organized on a different basis in the private shipyards and the Royal Dockyards. On the Tyne and Clyde, riveting gangs were paid according to how many rivets they had put in. A contract price was paid for a set figure. In theory the price reflected the speed at which the rivet could be driven down, and this in turn depended on its size. The figures were listed in a complex manner, for the price was regulated by the type of rivet being used, the location of the riveting work and whether the site was difficult and the work dangerous. The price was negotiated individually between the foreman and the gangs. Once it had been agreed, the riveters were told to get on with the job. USBISS played no role in these negotiations. Customary rates were, however, common to the particular yard and the district. Collective bargaining by USBISS officials at national and district level was primarily concerned with percentage increases or reductions to existing lists as a whole rather than the price of individual jobs. The union was also concerned over the question of apprentices, insisting on seven-year apprenticeships and a staggered entry into the trade. At the yard level the concern was with the peculiarities of the customized ship. Gangs of young riveters sometimes chased higher targets with the support of a foreman, but in general the rivet gangs knew that in any dispute other tradesmen would not do their work. Any significant undercutting would lead to various forms of social antagonism and was generally avoided. Many gangs were based on family networks or friendships. It has been suggested that 34 per cent of a commercial shipyard's supervisory labour costs was spent on riveting squads. In the Royal Dockyards the riveters were in a weaker position. The skilled labourers were not recognized as tradesmen and were not paid trade rates. The squads were frequently picked by foremen and chargehands. Dockyard riveters were paid on a time rate and did not have the scope for bargaining over the rate for rivets. They also worked a 48 hour week and had less chance of overtime work. This gave them a significantly lower wage than the riveters in the private yards. There were thus significant distinctions in manning and supervisory practices between the public and private sectors.

Caulking

Although very good riveting gave a watertight finish, it was caulking that really achieved this. This was done by using a seam tool to make a small furrow on the edge of the plate; a setting tool was then used by the caulker to cut a groove and the displaced material constituted the shoulder that was in contact with the next plate. If the edges of the plate were far apart, strips of iron were hammered in. Caulkers used light hammers, a splitting tool and a setting-in tool. This work was undertaken by individual caulkers who were paid piece rates. The straightforward nature of the work induced employers to introduce pneumatic machines for work on the shell

and decks. The employers, especially those in the north-east, were keen to reduce wages by 50–60 per cent from hand rates for those operatives who used the power tools for caulking. USBISS showed a keen interest in these trends and negotiated an agreement in 1905 whereby the tools, principally the pneumatic hammer, were to be allocated only to the members of the society. It did, however, agree to a wage reduction of 35–40 per cent for caulkers using this equipment.

Employers, Workers and the Trade Unions

Dreadnought construction involved a complex division of labour that was reflected in the sectionalized nature of the craft trade unions. There were twenty trade unions in the shipbuilding industry during the 1900s and almost 200 local transitory societies. A high degree of sectionalism existed in the yards and this fragmentation was reinforced by the spatial geography of the yards. High levels of trade union membership characterized the skilled trades in the private yards. They were able to have a considerable say on who was employed and what working practices were adopted. The Ship-constructors' and Shipwrights' Association (SSA) recruited among the loftsmen, draughtsmen and the shipwrights. It had a steady membership in the dockyards where the branches were considerably smaller than those at John Brown, Clydebank. Skilled workers kept to their own distinctive craft unions, as with the case of the pattern makers, who were usually members of the United Pattern Makers'

Society. The blacksmiths often chose to belong to regionally based trade societies, although a series of amalgamations between 1912 and 1914 created a national trade union. The draughtsmen working in the Tyne shipyards during the First World War were recruited into the Clyde-based Association of Engineering and Ship-building Draughtsmen, a small union that was still able to hold meetings of more than 350 draughtsmen on the Tyne in 1916. Riggers had their own society, while the Sailmakers' Society continued to exist in the Royal Dockyards.

The most influential and powerful trade union in the private sector was USBISS. This was a broad federation of trades and it recruited strongly among the platers, ironsmiths, riveters, caulkers and holders on. The earlier demarcation disputes of the 1890s with the SSA over the fairing of plates and the making of templates did not resurface during the 1900s, which was not a period of inter trade union rivalry. Instead, USBISS became involved in a series of conflicts with the Shipbuilding Employers' Federation (SEF). Its defence of craft practices involved limiting the adoption of mechanical riveting. The society was able to reassert unilateral action between 1911 and 1914 when it ended the practice of joint regulation with the employers. The society ensured that a squad of four was retained for riveting with no reduction in the wage rates for men using guns or machines. Wage reductions were, however, accepted for those drillers and caulkers who used pneumatic drills. Lower-paid apprentices were debarred from this work.

All of the shipyard trade unions had to recognize the enhanced power during the 1900s of the SEF, which attempted to embrace both shipbuilding and marine engineering. The federation was concentrated on the Clyde, the Tyne, the Wear and the Tees, with other major centres at Barrow, Belfast and Birkenhead. Approximately ninety firms were involved in the federation. The Clyde employers were the most hostile towards the trade unions, while north-east employers were inclined to recognize trade unions. The Tyne association had negotiated detailed agreements with drillers and platers' helpers in 1906. Comprehensive regional agreements had also been made in the north-east with USBISS. There were standing committees for each river to deal with yard issues. These committees negotiated on matters of piece rate, overtime payments and demarcation. No such agreements existed on the Clyde.

The pressure for a major redefinition of commercial and naval shipyard work relationships came from Armstrong Whitworth, Palmers, Vickers, Beardmore, Fairfield and John Brown. These firms were keen to weaken 'trade union interference', but they were not generally supported in the association by the more numerous and smaller family-based firms whose managerial and supervisory structures were less well developed. The federation's tensions with USBISS over managerial authority and labour discipline culminated in a national lock-out. On 16 August 1907 the SEF informed USBISS that the caulkers at the Walker yard of

Armstrong Whitworth had to end their strike over the employment of apprentice platers on caulking. The executive council of the society circulated its membership with a memorandum informing them that such a lock-out 'would entail a weekly expenditure which it is utterly impossible for us to meet'. The branches voted 8,341 to 2,903 for an immediate return to work. The SEF was intent on establishing a national agreement with USBISS to regulate piece rates and to make temporary decisions binding prior to discussions at local wages committees. The large naval firms also wanted to exploit the emerging slump in the shipping market to insist on wage reductions. It obtained a national agreement in March 1909 when seventeen trade unions signed an agreement that regulated general wage increases to 5 per cent. Under the terms of the agreement, no stoppages could occur before negotiations had taken place. Members of the union had to remain at work while the procedure was followed, even if the employer had changed the work conditions. USBISS had been keen to obtain notification of any proposed district changes in working practices and piecework rates and it wanted to introduce an element of neutral arbitration into the procedures. These positions were ignored by the SEF, which favoured the adoption of the Clyde practice of the discharge note, which was given to workers who struck despite the agreement on working procedures. The association also decided that the introduction of time clocks and job cards was to be a management prerogative.

Because of the 1909 agreement, USBISS fined its members at Palmers who went on strike, and in May 1910 the riveters who struck at Fairfield over the issue of a guaranteed minimum rate were forced to return to work because the SEF stated that their action was in breach of the agreement. Between 12 July and 18 August a further 14 shipyard stoppages occurred over piece rates: 5 on the Clyde and 6 on the Tyne, where Armstrong Whitworth workers struck on finding that a temporary management decision on riveting prices had led to the lowering of their wages. These disputes precipitated the enforcement of a national lock-out against USBISS between September and November 1910. When the agreement expired in March 1912, the local membership of USBISS emphatically voted for its non-renewal.

The outbreak of the First World War led to a further reassessment of shipyard working practices. On 3 November 1914 the national officials from the shipbuilding trade unions agreed that the rules governing working practices would be applied more flexibly and that such negotiations would occur at a local level. However, district officials were generally resistant to this, and USBISS and the SSA refused to allow any relaxation of trade union practices. The Admiralty became concerned over the prospect of unofficial strikes in the shipyards and was increasingly critical of the interventionist stance being adopted by the Ministry of Munitions. On 10 and 15 June 1916 the dilution commissioners reached a labour agreement with the Clyde-based committee of the SSA and USBISS. The central issues were the dilution of skilled labour through the recruitment of female labour, the demarcation of work and apprenticeships. The Admiralty remained concerned about the situation affecting warship construction and in October 1916 it was given full control in labour matters in all war shipbuilding firms on condition that it accepted the Ministry of Munitions' labour priority firms. This agreement, however, soon foundered. Subsequently a Shipyard Labour Department was set up in the Admiralty where an influential faction sought to restrain the impact of dilution and to prevent fundamental changes in existing working practices because it thought that such activities would create serious disruption to warship construction.

In this era, industrial relations in the shipyards varied from region to region. In Scotland many shipyard workers in Dalmuir, Govan and Partick became involved in the campaigns of 1915 and 1916 against local landlords because of high rent levels and evictions. Disputes also occurred at Fairfield and Beardmore over complaints that shipyard workers who refused to do dirty work were threatened with dismissal without a working certificate. After these protests, some of the terms of the Munitions Act were changed through discussions with the trade unions: the format of the leaving certificate was altered and the financial penalties that courts were allowed to impose were significantly reduced. On the Tyne and Wear the relationship between the employers and the local officials of the shipbuilding trade unions was more harmonious. In 1917 the Tyne Shipbuilders' Association stated that:

'there is no serious unrest amongst workers in the shipyards in this district as far as relations between employers and workmen are concerned . . . such unrest as does exist . . . is largely one of economics brought by the methods adopted hitherto in the lack of control of prices and unequal distribution of food.'

The trade union officials on the Tyne and Wear offered no hostile evidence to the commissioners, who in their report praised the trade unions for 'adjusting labour difficulties' and 'bringing about good relations between employers and employed on the North East coast'. The trade union district officials were prepared to support patriotic warship production, but they were also able to secure substantial pay increases for their members during the war. At Palmers, the smiths' wages rose from the prewar rate of 47*s* 10*d* to 60*s* 9*d* in October 1915, the wages of platers moved from 59*s* 6*d* to 72*s* 2*d*, and those of riveters went from 43*s* 3*d* to 50*s*. These improvements occurred without any fundamental changes being made to working practices.

Trade union activity in the Royal Dockyards was more muted than in the private yards because the Admiralty was opposed to directly admitting the trade unions into direct negotiations with dockyard officials or itself. Instead it insisted on the archaic practice of annual petitions. While this method of consultation appeared to be egalitarian – a dockyard worker could have his case discussed by a series of local officers, including charge hands, inspectors and foremen, then finally the Admiral Superintendent – the collective experience of the broad dockyard classes was largely negative. Nearly all significant dockyard petitions were turned down between 1905 and 1913. One of the most important issues was the dockyard men's views on the inferiority of their wages in comparison with the earnings available on the Clyde and Tyne. Dockyard men worked 48 hours a week, without overtime, compared with the 54 hours worked in several prominent yards. They said that most dockyard tradesmen were not getting the going rate for the job. The skilled labourers were also unsuccessful in their efforts to obtain trade recognition. The Admiralty justified its stance in terms of peculiar dockyard practices. In particular it referred to the advantages of men being placed on the establishment list. These men were guaranteed continuity of employment, albeit at lower rates than hired men, and also a dockyard pension when they retired at sixty-five years of age (if they lived to receive it). These pensions could not be passed on to a surviving wife. However, for several years, principally between 1905 and 1910, the establishment was closed because of the Treasury's concern over dockyard wage costs. When a hired dockyard worker reached the age of forty he was no longer considered for

establishment. In some trades, such as joiners, smiths, hammermen, plumbers, there were more established men than hired, up to a 75 per cent ratio. However, in the most numerous trades the ratios were much smaller, under a third, as with the case of the skilled labourers and ship fitters. The Treasury had advised that the yearly establishment average should remain at 25 per cent, although this had fallen as low as 13 per cent by 1910 in several of the major trades. Dockyard men undoubtedly appreciated the security that establishment gave them and waged an effective campaign to increase the percentages of establishment between 1913 and 1915. Dockyard superintendents and the director of dockyards strongly approved of the establishment list as a stratagem for diluting the impact of trade unionism within the yards.

The shipwrights were traditionally the elite stratum of workers in the Royal Dockyards. They were subject to the idiosyncratic practice of the annual shoal when the senior charge hands picked their squad for the next year by rotation. This offered the opportunity to break up any established close friendships in the squads that aroused their suspicion. Familial networking could only occur if the charge hand was in agreement. Such an institution weakened the role of the shipwrights' trade union. The annual Portsmouth trades council reports of 1912 and 1913 reveal trade union affiliations from the ASE (branches 1–5), the SSA (branches A, B and C), USBISS, the Smiths and Hammermen, Copper Smiths,

Smiths and Hammermen, Copper Smiths, Iron Founders, Riggers, Sailmakers, Pattern Makers, and the Government Labourers' Union. Several shipwrights only attended 4 or 5 times out of a possible 24 meetings, a trend that was continued among the majority of USBISS delegates. Individual members, like the shipwrights Mactavish and Littlewood, and the smiths and hammermen Roberts and Beere, were active in both industrial affairs and the ILP, but dockyard workers were rarely collectively militant. The ASE merely threatened an overtime ban in 1913 and efforts to mount a joint campaign with the shipwrights failed.

A view from the head of no. 5 slipway of Portsmouth Dockyard, Monday 2 October 1905. The middle line blocks on which the *Dreadnought* will be built are being checked for straightness and declivity. The two v-shaped poles in the foreground are sheer legs which will hoist the stem casting into place. (PCL)

Portsmouth Dockyard, later on the same day. The blocks have been set up and one of the after bulkheads has been positioned. At the far end of the slip can be seen the stem casting which has been hoisted into position. (PCL)

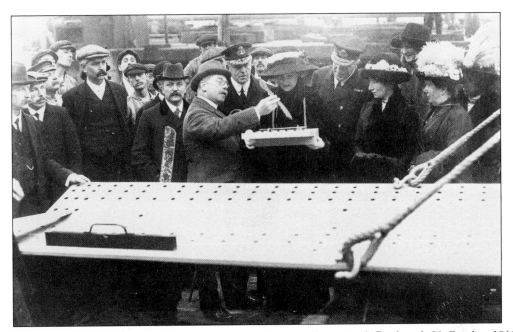

Laying the keel plate of the battleship HMS *Queen Elizabeth* at Portsmouth Dockyard, 21 October 1912.
Mr J. Apsey, head of the Construction Department, presents a silver ink stand in the form of a keel plate
to the Honourable Lady Hedworth-Meux, wife of the Commander-in-Chief (pictured centre). (PCL)

The battleship HMS *Queen Elizabeth* on no. 5 slip, Portsmouth Dockyard, 1913. The height of the blocks
on the left of the picture would suggest that this is the after cut-up of the stern and the camera is looking
into what will form the lower machinery space of 'X' 15 inch turret. Although the hull plating is well
advanced the stern casting and after cut-up have yet to be erected. (PCL)

The building berth of the battle-cruiser HMS *Hood*, September 1916. The centre line blocks support the outer flat keel and frame sections, which show lightening holes in their centre. One would assume she had no single vertical keel plate but was built with two keel plates, one on each side of the frame section, forming a box. It would appear that the ground-ways, on which the vessel will be launched, are in the process of being built. The stacked timber will form props to support the structure of the ship as it is being built. (BRCUG)

The main deck of the battle-cruiser HMS *Hood*. This deck would eventually be plated with 2 inch armour, which increased to 3 inch over magazines. The peculiar round-down and slope of the deck were to assist the armour protection and were some 10 ft inside the ship. (BRCUG)

The battle-cruiser HMS *Hood*, afloat after launching. A section of 12 inch thick barbette armour is being lowered into position for 'A' turret. Armour was tongue

and grooved on its butt edges, which locked it into position. Here the groove of
the butt is clearly visible. (BRCUG)

John Brown's Shipyard, Clydebank, 14 April 1915. The outer flat keel of the battle-cruiser HMS *Repulse* is being erected. The *Repulse* was 794 ft in length and too long for the slipway, which had to be extended over the railway lines and roadway. The centre line blocks supporting the keel plate have been made into a low bridge to allow traffic to pass under the ship while it is being built. (BRCUG)

John Brown's, Clydebank, 14 April 1915. Looking forward along the starboard side of the *Repulse* as the elegant underwater shape of the battle-cruiser begins to emerge, with the erection of the lower bulkheads up to the Lower and Platform deck levels. (BRCUG)

HMS *Repulse*, 5 May 1915. Looking forward from the forward engine-room into the after boiler room before the erection of the engine-room bulkhead. The deck beams are up to Lower deck level. The deep bottom frames will either form the inner bottom tanks for storing fuel, oil and water, or become airspaces such as coffer dams that form safety barriers between tanks; the inner bottom plating is in the process of being laid. (BRCUG)

The battle-cruiser HMS *Repulse*, 6 October 1915. A view from the stern showing the after barbette. On joining the fleet, the *Repulse* and *Renown* were severely criticized for their lack of armour. During firing trials of the main armament, the hull was strained and both ships spent long periods in dockyard hands, earning them the nicknames of Refit and Repair. (BRCUG)

John Brown's, Clydebank. Looking along the inner flat keel of the *Repulse* from frame no. 44. Compressed air formed the motive power for many of the riveting, caulking and drilling machines used in the shipbuilding industry at this time. A Boyer's pneumatic drill can be seen in the middle of the picture with its air line running down the keel plate. Workmen are in the process of reaming the rivet holes before final closing of plates for riveting. (BRCUG)

The battle-cruiser HMS *Repulse* under construction at John Brown's, Clydebank, 8 July 1916. The picture belies her 90 ft beam, but shows the flare of her graceful bow; at 32.6 knots she was the fastest capital ship in the world and with her sister, *Renown*, set a new world record for construction of that size of vessel, of twenty months. (BRCUG)

John Brown's, Clydebank, September 1913. Setting up the forward frames and deck beams to the Platform deck of the battleship HMS *Barham*. (BRCUG)

John Brown's, Clydebank, 6 September 1913. A view of the stern of the *Barham*. The stern casting has been hoisted into position by the sheer legs. (BRCUG)

HMS *Barham* on the day of her launch, 31 October 1914. The teak planking that formed the backing to her side armour can be clearly seen in the armour recess on the side of the ship. (BRCUG)

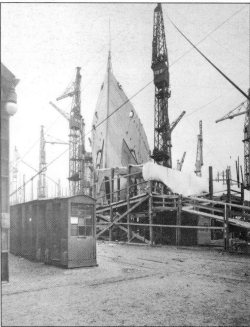

Above: HMS *Tiger* being built at John Brown & Co., 6 September 1913. She was the last coal-burning British capital ship and the only battle-cruiser to mount 6 inch guns. Plating at the fore end is up to the weather deck and the three hawse pipes are in position. Deck beams in way of the two forward turrets have yet to be cut away for the barbettes. (BRCUG)

Left: The battle-cruiser HMS *Tiger* at John Brown's, Clydebank, 15 December 1913. (BRCUG)

The weather deck of **HMS** *Tiger*, viewed from aft, 5 December 1913. The curve of the ship's side and deck in the lower right-hand corner of the picture shows the after starboard 6 inch battery. The *Tiger* was launched on 15 December 1913. (BRCUG)

The *Dreadnought* under construction at Portsmouth Dockyard, Saturday 28 October 1905,
looking aft along the main deck. Illumination at night was provided by electric lights,

searchlights and lucal lamps. One can be seen to the left of the large hole in the deck. These were pressurized lamps that produced a large 6 ft flame similar to a blow lamp. (PCL)

4: Launching Dreadnoughts

An obvious distinction between the privately owned shipyards and the dockyards was the degree of attention given to the launch of Dreadnoughts in the Royal Dockyards. Crowds of 60,000 came to Portsmouth Dockyard on a Saturday morning to watch the launch of HMS *Iron Duke* (12 October 1912); as many as 80,000 are said to have attended the HMS *Queen Elizabeth* launch on Saturday 16 October 1913. These public spectacles expressed deep-seated and authoritative values. Each of the launches had its distinct coterie of admirals, aristocrats, politicians, naval officers, senior dockyard officials, their wives and daughters, and the massed ranks of manual workers. In matters of detail, individual launches differed from earlier and subsequent launches, although what stands out throughout these forms of naval spectacle are the powerful unifying trends: a common administrative practice and a repetition of forms, pageantry and ritual that were utilized on launch days.

A launch involved two ceremonies. The first was the naming of the ship. This was performed by a 'great lady'. In the case of HMS *Iron Duke*, this was the Duchess of Wellington, and for HMS *Queen Elizabeth* it was Lady Hedworth-Meux, the wife of the Commander-in-Chief. At a given signal the lady swung the bottle of Australian wine against the Dreadnought's bows and uttered the traditional words: 'I wish good luck to the *Iron Duke* and to all those who sail in her.' This ceremony was accompanied by a burst of spontaneous cheering. After a slight pause and on a given signal, the skilled labourers waiting beneath the ship knocked out the final block restraining her. On the launch platform the head of the construction department removed a chisel from the launch box, which was made from HMS *Victory*'s timbers, and then handed it to the lady guest who struck it with a mallet, severing the launch rope, which was situated at the bows on an oak rosette. The cutting of the rope released the half ton weights that knocked aside the last of the dog shores. The ship then began to creep along the grease-coated ground ways. As the ship's momentum increased, the crowds cheered vigorously, waving hats and handkerchiefs, while the sirens of naval ships in the harbour sounded out. The Royal Marine band always played 'Rule Britannia' as the Dreadnought steadily gathered momentum down the slip. The impact of the cacophony of sounds – the clattering restraining chains, the grinding hull and the cheering of the crowds – was magnified by the exciting visual spectacle of the Dreadnought entering the harbour waters. For many observers these were quasi-magical moments of grandeur; a time to express and articulate deeply held imperial values.

Beneath the surface spectacle a launch ceremony was the site of preplanned expectations, for the officials who arranged these ceremonial events were confident that the grand event would always function in a splendid manner. Most of the workers and their families had already seen several other launches, yet masses of people were undoubtedly thrilled and affected by the spectacle. A momentary sense of a social solidarity was achieved. Spontaneous moments reproduced memorable moments, as for instance when the dockyard workers clambered onto the slip to watch the final entry of the Dreadnought into the harbour waters. The administrators also had the seating in the south stand placed very close to the hull to enhance the ship's towering presence. The harbour setting with the moored HMS *Victory*, the lines of naval warships, plus neighbouring docks and buildings produced a scenic vista for this grand occasion. A Royal Dockyard Dreadnought launch always released powerful conformist sentiments: it was a national communion where the representatives of the national elite, the armed services and local society reaffirmed their commitment to the Royal Navy and the monarchy. These values were part of a wider frame of reference that reinforced a particular social order – an order that held particular assumptions about Englishness, Empire, great power status and the country's glorious naval traditions. Such evocations of imperial power in the 1900s were rarely exercised by the elites in a brutal and arbitrary manner; instead it was cloaked in an effective spectacle.

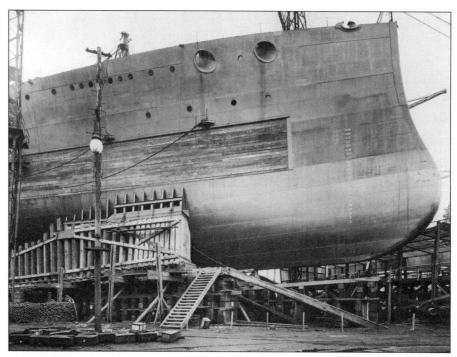

John Brown, Clydebank, HMS *Tiger*, 15 December 1913. A side profile of the head of the ways and the forward cradle. (BRCUG)

John Brown, Clydebank, HMS *Repulse*, 8 January 1916. The last of the temporary shores are removed a few hours before she takes to the water. (BRCUG)

Portsmouth Dockyard, HMS *Neptune* launch, 30 September 1909. The Duchess of Albany performed the ceremony, which was watched by Mr James Marshall, Director of the Royal Dockyards. Dockyard workers on the slipway anticipate the final convergence of ship and water, while others give three hearty cheers. A solitary Royal Marine Artillery bandsman has left the band's concert platform to get a better view of HMS *Neptune*'s baptism. This image, like several other photographs taken by Silk and Cribb, evocatively captures in a stylized manner the excitement and collective enthusiasm of launch day. (PCL)

Beardmore, Dalmuir, HMS *Ramillies*, 12 September 1916. Profile of the ship showing the Arrol gantry system. It measured 750 × 135 ft and was 150 ft high. There were four travelling cranes on each gantry side, which allowed eight squads of platers and riveters to work supported by cranes. (BRCUG)

Beardmore, Dalmuir, HMS *Ramillies*, 12 September 1916. The forefoot of the battleship is on the right of the picture waiting for her baptism as spectators on the VIP stand pose for the photographer. (BRCUG)

Beardmore, Dalmuir, HMS *Ramillies*, 12 September 1916, stern view. (BRCUG)

Portsmouth Dockyard, HMS *Royal Sovereign* launch, 29 April 1915. Lady Dalmeny is instructed by the manager of the Portsmouth Dockyard Constructive Department, Mr J. Apsey, on her duties and procedure in the naming and launch ceremonies. Rear-Admiral Hedworth Meux looks on. (PCL)

John Brown, Clydebank, HMS *Hood* launch, 22 August 1918. John Brown workers watch the ship. In general the launches in the shipyards did not have any of the conspicuous pomp of the Royal Dockyard launches. The launch weight of HMS *Hood* was 21,920 tons, although this included 200 tons of buoyancy with the bilge ways. The hull structure was complete up to the forecastle except for the openings for the main machinery. There was no structure above the forecastle deck except the plating behind the armour of the conning tower erection and the aft screen bulkheads. On the starboard side of the hull, none of the side armour had been fitted apart from plates 16 and 17. The boilers were aboard but not the main machinery. (BRCUG)

Portsmouth Dockyard, HMS *King George V* launch, 9 October 1911. Flags of the Empire drape the VIP stand, while a naval guard of honour waits to present arms to Princess Christian of Schleswig-Holstein and her entourage, who are due to arrive by carriage at the foot of the steps leading to the platform. The band of the Royal Marine Artillery is to the left. Dockyard workers gaze down from the ship's rails. The invited VIP guests were Princess Christian of Schleswig-Holstein, Princess Victoria (her daughter), Sir Arthur Moore (Commander-in-Chief), the Honourable Evelyn Moore (his sister), Alderman Sir T. Scott Foster (Mayor of Portsmouth), Rear Admiral C.J. Briggs (Controller of the Navy and Third Sea Lord), Mrs Briggs, Rear Admiral Herbert King Hall (Director of Naval Mobilization), Lady Margaret

King Hall, Rear Admiral Troubridge (Private Secretary to the First Lord), Mrs Troubridge, Maj.-Gen. William Nicholls (Deputy Adjutant General of the Royal Marines), Mr F.W. Black (Director of Naval Contracts), Mrs Black, Sir J.B. Marshall (Director of Dockyards and Dockyard Labour), Lady Marshall, Engineer Commander J.W. Horn (Engineer Assistant to the Director of Dockyards), John Apsey (Manager of the Construction Department, Portsmouth Dockyard), J.S. Sanders (Manager of the Engineering Department, Portsmouth Dockyard), Mr M.J. Maguinness (Constructor) and various managing directors from Sir W.G. Armstrong Whitworth and Co. Ltd, W. Beardmore and Co., Harland and Wolff, Palmers Shipyard and Iron Works, Scotts, the Thames Iron Works and Vickers Ltd. (PCL)

Portsmouth Dockyard, HMS *King George V* launch, 9 October 1911. Shipwrights knock out the shores of the building blocks at the after end of the ship a few days before the launch. (PCL)

Portsmouth Dockyard, HMS *King George V* launch, 9 October 1911. The ship is moored 200 yd from no. 5 slip as the crowd wanders over the ways and disperses. The panoramic image has been taken from the VIP platform and seeks to convey a visual context for the concluding moments of launch day. (PCL)

Portsmouth Dockyard, launch of HMS *Queen Elizabeth*, 16 October 1913. A large assembled crowd in the south enclosure awaits the ceremonies. The launch ceremony was performed by Lady Hedworth-Meux, the wife of the Commander-in-Chief. (PCL)

Portsmouth Dockyard, HMS *Queen Elizabeth* launch, 16 October 1913. Dockyard workers emerge from the assembled crowd and climb on the slip to watch the ship enter the harbour waters. (PCL)

Portsmouth Dockyard, launch of HMS *Dreadnought*, 10 February 1906. The northern section of

the crowd stands patiently awaiting the arrival of King Edward VII. (PCL)

Portsmouth Dockyard, HMS *Dreadnought* launch, 10 February 1906. An impressive image that lends support to the articles in the local newspapers, which suggested that crowds of 60,000 people and more attended these Dreadnought launches. (PCL)

Portsmouth Dockyard, HMS *Dreadnought* launch, 10 February 1906. As the crowd disperses, several curious workmen explore the ways and one young boy hails the cameraman. (PCL)

Portsmouth Dockyard, building slip no. 5, HMS *Bellerophon*, 27 July 1907, setting the cradle on to the *Bellerophon*. Some 500 dockyard shipwrights hammer in long wooden wedges, which were placed between the bilge ways and the poppet boards for the entire length of the Dreadnought. The hammering was commenced from the stern at low tide, while the strikes were coordinated to the chimes of a bell. 'Setting up' involved transferring the dead weight of the ship's hull from the building blocks to the cradles, which would carry the ship into the harbour waters. (PCL)

Portsmouth Dockyard, HMS *Bellerophon* launch, 27 July 1907. Dockyard workers standing on the front of the lower platform give three hearty cheers for the ship. (PCL)

Portsmouth Dockyard, HMS *Iron Duke* launch, 12 October 1912. The Duchess of Wellington uses the traditional wooden mallet and chisel to cut the rope, which will release the ship's suspended weights. (PCL)

Portsmouth Dockyard, HMS *Iron Duke* launch. An awed response from the platform as VIPs watch the *Iron Duke* descend the ways. Those in attendance on the VIP platform included the Duchess of Wellington, the Duke of Wellington, Admiral Sir Hedworth-Meux (Commander-in-Chief), Lady Hedworth-Meux, Sir J. Forcey (Director of Dockyard Stores), Rear Admiral H.L. Heath (Admiral Superintendent of Portsmouth Dockyard), Vice Admiral Sir H.B. Jackson (Head of the War College), Sir John Scott (Lord Mayor of Portsmouth), Mrs Scott (Lady Mayoress), Admiral Charles Beresford MP, Bertram Falle MP, Mrs Falle, Mr Winston Churchill MP (First Lord of the Admiralty), Mrs Churchill, Sir William Nicholas (Adjutant General of the Royal Marines), Sir James Marshall (Director of Dockyards), Lady Marshall, Mr F.W. Black (Director of Naval Contracts), Captain E.S. Alexander-Sinclair (Paymaster-in-Chief), Commander A. Bromley, Lieutenant M. Boissier, Rear Admiral Wishart (Engineer), Colonel M. Oldfield, Colonel L.J. Pease, Mr G. Hammond-Etherton (Clerk to Portsmouth), and heads of dockyard departments Mr J. Apsey, Mr W. Renny and Mr Drummer. (PCL)

Portsmouth Dockyard, HMS *Iron Duke* launch. The local photographer has managed to frame the ship's profile. (PCL)

Portsmouth Dockyard, HMS *Iron Duke* launch, 12 October 1912. Dockyard workmen collect the floating slum, which greased the slipway, from the harbour waters after the launch. This scene was frequently reproduced on local postcards. (PCL)

5: FITTING-OUT:
Superstructure, Propulsion and Armaments

Vickers, Armstrong Whitworth, Beardmore and John Brown supplied the main machinery for their own Dreadnoughts. However, the Admiralty insisted that other firms competed among each other for work after the main contractor had been decided. At Portsmouth Dockyard the HMS *Queen Elizabeth* machinery contract was given to the Wallsend Slipway and Engineering Company. The main machinery involved were twenty-four Babcock and Wilcox boilers and their accompanying fittings: the stop valves, steam pipes, main feed valves, water gauges, air cocks, test cocks, pressure gauge cocks, circulating valves and emptying valves. The Parsons turbines were made at the Wallsend Slipway Engineering Company under licence. The auxiliary machinery purchased for HMS *Queen Elizabeth* included feed pumps, air pumps, condensers, circulating water pumps, lubrication pumps, turning engines, steering gear (Napier Brothers), evaporators, distillers (G.J. Weir, Cathcart), capstan engines, electric light engines and generators. The refrigeration and ice-making machinery was manufactured by the Liverpool Refrigeration Company. The Admiralty imposed rigid schedules that itemized the powers of the overseers in terms of their appointment and their powers with regard to inspecting and rejecting work, plus requesting drawings and sketches of parts. In the dockyards the gun mountings and heavy armament were supplied by Armstrong Whitworth or Vickers, whose workers supervised their installation. Dockyard engine fitters petitioned the Admiralty in 1913 and 1914 for permission to undertake this work, but their request was denied.

The range of work tasks required in fitting-out was more varied and complex than that associated with the erection of the hull. Decks were subdivided into cabins, messes, storage rooms, magazines and workshops; miles of electric cabling had to be laid; and ladderways and lifts installed. On such large ships the effectiveness of the ventilation system was essential – it was achieved by the use of electrical fans and a comprehensive network of ventilation trunking. The main deck of the Queen Elizabeth class had fourteen sets of $12\frac{1}{2}$ inch fans with electric heaters and motors along with eight sets of $7\frac{1}{2}$ inch fans with heaters. Large vent-trunking was also employed to bring cool air to the boiler rooms, while the magazine rooms were cooled by refrigeration machinery. The upper and main deck plans of the designated flagships, HMS *Iron Duke* and HMS *Queen Elizabeth*, itemize the extensive number of areas that were required for a ship's company of 2,000 men. In some cases the furnishings were lavish, most obviously in the admiral's quarters. His suite of rooms contained bookcases, tables, a rolltop writing desk, settees, book racks, cupboards, large sideboards, a silver cabinet, wardrobes and chests of drawers. The chief stokers' and naval artificers' messes, by way of contrast, were much more simple and consisted of a table and lockers, while the sailors' and stokers' messes had ditty box lockers. A variety of equipment had to be brought on board. Some pieces related to the ship's galleys and involved boilers, sinks, dressers and racks. The sick bay in the forward section of the main deck had to be built, and tables, stools, lockers, wash basins, baths, lavatories and urinal troughs had to be installed. On the lower decks, storage rooms had to be built for paint, canvas, cordage, bunting, food and ammunition.

Dockyard workers employed on fitting-out worked a different regime from those employed on the erection of the hull. In June 1911 an agreement was concluded between the dockyard shipwrights and the Admiralty over a 51 hour week. On the day shift there was a 1 hour break per day. From Monday to Thursday the hours were 7.00 a.m. to 12.00 p.m. and 1.00 to 5.00 p.m. Those of Friday and Saturday were 7.00 a.m. to 12.00 p.m. and 1.00 to 6.00 p.m. Sunday morning was worked between 7.00 a.m. and 12.00 p.m. On night shifts, which were worked when needed on five consecutive nights, two 45 minute breaks were allowed between 10.00 and 10.45 p.m., and between 2.30 and 3.15 a.m. The shift lasted from 6.00 p.m. to 7.00 a.m., and the rate of pay was time and a quarter for all hours. A Dreadnought became a complex and, at times, confused workplace. Work sites ranged through the freshwater tanks, the oil fuel compartments and the feedtanks of the double bottom, to the boiler and engine rooms, the magazines, the steering compartments and the watertight compartments of the hold, upwards through the lower deck, to the platform deck, to the middle and main decks, the upper deck and the forecastle deck. Superstructure work involved the erection of the funnels, conning tower, masts and compass platform. On the lower decks, ship fitters and engine fitters had to master the intricacies of boiler and turbine design, even if they were supervised by the contractor's employees. Rigid demarcations existed, because the work undertaken by the electricians and engine fitters in the Royal Dockyards could not be undertaken by skilled labourers. Engine fitters in their 1913 and 1914 petitions had sought the Admiralty's permission to work on boiler room gratings, handrails, ladders and the hydraulic systems. These requests were all denied. Between 1912 and 1914, the skilled labourers had also requested increased payments for their own riveting work with high-tension rivets, which were used for deck plates and bulkheads, but this request was again denied by the Admiralty.

The distinct work gangs required to work in dispersed locations meant there was little of the homogeneity associated with the collective work in hull erection. An indication of the varied nature of this work can be understood with reference to the men working at the lower levels of the conning tower of HMS *Queen Elizabeth*. Different gangs of men had to build hatches, five ladderways and four skylights, fit out the navigation officer's cabin, the officers' WCs, the rooms for the officers' oilskins, and install the ventilator shafts to the engine room. The ship's conning tower required the installation of sounding machines, semaphore machines, searchlight controllers, Evershed transmitters, Vickers range clocks, the revolution telegraph, the engine telegraph, the steering wheel and various communication tubes. The tower was protected by 15 inch armour plate made by Armstrong Whitworth, Elswick, while the control tower armour was made at Beardmore and the plate for the roof of the rangefinder came from the Hecla Works, Sheffield. The 15 inch gun Barr and Stroud rangefinder was sited in the control tower, which was mounted on top of the conning tower. This kind of fitting required complex scheduling from the

foremen in order to achieve an effective rotation of the gangs. Inspection and supervision were vital matters in terms of achieving the qualitative build required by an Admiralty contract. Planning of the work routines for platers and riveters, ship and engine fitters, carpenters and painters required prompt regulation. Management delegated most of this supervision to charge hands, inspectors and foremen, whose responsibility it was to visit the men on the job.

Dock Inspections

These followed standard procedures in the private shipyards and the Royal Dockyards. Admiralty letters of 7 August 1915 informed the Wallsend Slipway Company that HMS *Queen Elizabeth* was to be ready for steam trials in December 1915. The letter detailed that the turrets and guns had to be placed onboard, the turbines had to be lined up with the shaftings and complete connections were to be established with all of the turbines. Water tests were to be conducted on the main steam pipes, the feed section lines, the condensers and oil feed pipes. Dockyard officials were instructed to provide the additional auxiliary boilers that were required when the hydraulic machinery was tested. The final dockyard inspections occurred on 25 January 1915. They involved the ship's engines, for, although the hydraulic system was tested, it could only be finally assessed at the gunnery trials. The boilers were inspected and steam was raised in each boiler, but they were not tried at full power because the ship remained moored. Particular care was taken over measuring the expansion of the turbine blades and their freedom of movement. The engine room ventilation was checked and the closed exhaust fittings tested. The electrical machinery and wiring, including the refrigeration and electrical motors, were inspected and passed. Tests were carried out on the ship's electrical bells, telephones and hoists. The rigging, magazines and bilges were inspected. A longer sequence of inspections had been carried out earlier (1 December 1914–5 January 1915), when the bulk-heads and double bottom had been inspected. Surveys were made of the inner and outer surfaces of the plates, from the waterline to the double bottom, and then from the waterline to the topside. The wing components were the most difficult to reach. These surveys also included the cooking galley, the ammunition hoists, the boat hoists and the derricks. The inspections revealed that a considerable amount of work remained to be completed in the engine room, where there was incomplete lagging of the oil pipes in boiler room 1, while the starboard drainpipes to the heating had not been completed, nor were the exhaust pipes finished. New scheduling was agreed. Additional work was also undertaken on the coffer dam built in the engine rooms.

Superstructure

John Brown, Clydebank, 9 March 1915, HMS *Barham*. The machinery housing to 'X' barbette being lifted onboard. (BRCUG)

John Brown, Clydebank, 9 March 1915, HMS *Barham*. 'X' barbette being lowered into position. (BRCUG)

John Brown, Clydebank, 17 May 1915, HMS *Barham*. A 15 inch gun barrel for 'X' turret being lifted into position; each barrel weighed 98 tons. The gun barrel is suspended from a 150 ton tower crane. (BRCUG)

John Brown, Clydebank, 7 June 1915, HMS *Barham*. The rollers and gearing of 'B' turret are exposed. (BRCUG)

John Brown, Clydebank, 8 July 1915. Profile of HMS *Barham*. Between 1914 and 1918, John Brown built the battleship HMS *Barham*, the battle-cruiser HMS *Repulse*, 2 light cruisers (*Canterbury* and *Ceres*), a sea plane carrier, 35 destroyers and 3 'E' class submarines. (BRCUG)

John Brown, Clydebank, 5 April 1916, HMS *Repulse*. The imposing tripod mast and fore funnel have been completed. (BRCUG)

John Brown, Clydebank, 21 April 1916, HMS *Repulse*. Five distinct types of crane are being deployed at the fitting-out basin. The second 15 inch gun for 'A' turret has been placed onboard prior to the completion of the turret roofs. (BRCUG)

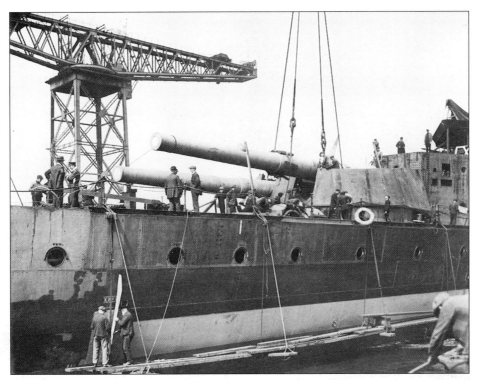

John Brown, Clydebank, 18 May 1916, HMS *Repulse*. A 15 inch gun barrel for the 'Y' turret being lowered into position. The 150 ton Arrol hammerhead crane profile dominates the yard skyline. (BRCUG)

John Brown, Clydebank, 8 August 1916, HMS *Repulse*. Impressive view of the forward 15 inch Mark I guns. For the first time in British battle-cruisers there were two directors, one on the foremast and the other in the armoured hood on the conning tower roof. (BRCUG)

John Brown, Clydebank, 15 July 1916, HMS *Repulse*. Profile of the fitting-out basin. The Arrol electric derrick cranes clustering around the building slip dominate the skyline. They were originally purchased for the building of the Cunard liner *Lusitania* in 1906. 'A' and 'B' turrets have been completed. (BRCUG)

John Brown, Clydebank, 13 August 1916, HMS *Repulse* raising steam. The ship's main armament was praised by contemporary naval commentators, although the triple 4 inch Mark I gun mountings were subsequently criticized for being difficult to operate. (BRCUG)

John Brown, Clydebank, 4 August 1914, HMS *Tiger*. The three equally spaced funnels gave the *Tiger* a grace that pleased the eye of all who saw her. In 1917 the searchlight platforms gave way to searchlight towers, fitted around the third funnel. The tripod foremast, with its high topmast and armament director at the foretop, has yet to be fully built. (BRCUG)

The forward 13.5 inch guns of HMS *Conqueror*. A gang of dockyard workers examine the plating on the roof of 'A' turret. (PCL)

John Brown, Clydebank, 2 December 1919, HMS *Hood*. Steam is being raised in the forward boilers. The 15 inch guns have been fitted in 'A' and 'B' turrets but remain exposed to the elements. The general offices are visible in the centre of the image. The unusual stature of the large conning tower and the observation tower is dramatically realized in this photograph. The base of the conning tower extended down to the main deck. Its main structure consisted of two shells with 11 and 9 inch armour in the upper sections. The two shells were linked by a narrow passage. The conning tower armour weighed 600 tons and the whole structure 900 tons. (BRCUG)

John Brown, Clydebank, HMS *Hood*, 8 March 1920. The morning shift leaves the ship. (BRCUG)

Propulsion

Vickers, Barrow-in-Furness, the turbine shop. Two types of naval turbine were used in Dreadnought battleships and battle-cruisers. Parsons developed reaction turbines, while John Brown, Clydebank, undertook a joint development with the US firm Curtis to produce impulse turbines. Parsons direct-drive turbines were fitted to British Dreadnoughts between 1906 and 1914 (HMS *Dreadnought*, Invincible class, Bellerophon class, St Vincent class, Indefatigable class, Colossus class, HMS *Neptune*, Orion class, Lion class, King George V class, Iron Duke class, HMS *Erin* and HMS *Agincourt*). HMS *Canada* had a mixture of Brown-Curtis and Parsons turbines (1911–14). Brown and Curtis direct-drive turbines were fitted to HMS *Tiger* (1912–14), while in the Queen Elizabeth class (1912–16) Brown and Curtis turbines were used on HMS *Barham* and HMS *Valiant* and Parsons turbines for HMS *Queen Elizabeth*, HMS *Warspite* and HMS *Malaya*. The Renown class (1915–16) had Brown and Curtis turbines, the Royal Sovereign Class (1913–16) had Parsons turbines, the Glorious class (1915–17) had Parsons turbines and HMS *Furious* (1915–17) and HMS *Hood* (1916–20) had Brown and Curtis turbines. (VSEL)

Vickers, Barrow-in-Furness, turbines for the battleship **HMS** *Vanguard*. The upper cast-iron cylinder weighed approximately 36 tons, a cast turbine rotor drum weighed 22 tons, a ribbed rotor drum 17 tons, a rotor wheel 26 tons and a steel tube for the spindle 70 tons. (VSEL)

Vickers, Barrow-in-Furness, turbines for the battle-cruiser HMS *Lion*.

In reaction turbines, steam passes through a continuous ring of fixed blades, and is directed by them upon the first ring of moving blades. This changes the direction of flow, after which the steam comes into contact with the second ring of fixed blades, where the direction of flow is again changed. The steam then enters the second set of moving blades, and in like manner passes through succeeding stages, at each stage the diameter of the rings is increased. The steam, therefore, had more space as it goes through the turbine, and the whole expansion takes place as it passes through the blades . . . Reaction turbines rotate at slower speeds than do impulse turbines.

A.E. Ingham, *Machine Construction and Drawing*, Book II, 1914.

Parsons reaction turbines had small radial clearances and with the early turbines the blade tips were susceptible to damage from distortion of the rotor, particularly when being 'warmed up' before operation. Brazed segmental blades with side locking pieces were adopted to overcome this problem. (VSEL)

Vickers, Barrow-in-Furness, two sets of low-pressure turbines for HMS *Lion*. These produced 70,000 s.h.p. Each set consisted of HP and LP ahead turbines and HP and LP astern turbines. The HP had a cruising stage at the forward end for working at low power. The steam passed over this stage by means of a special bypass when the turbines ran at higher power. The photograph reveals the aft ends of the low-pressure turbines, showing the bed plate connections and the system of stays in the exhaust branch. It also shows the turning gear and its electrical motor. (PCL)

Vickers, Barrow-in-Furness, foundry. (VSEL)

John Brown, Clydebank, turbine erecting shop. The firm acquired a licence for the construction of Parsons turbines in 1903 and received a licence from Curtis in 1908 to undertake joint development work on naval turbines. Curtis-Brown impulse turbines were different from Parsons turbines in having a single cylinder: the complete range of expansion from boiler steam to condenser pressure was carried out in the one turbine. (BRCUG)

John Brown, Clydebank, brass finishing shop. Brass was used for underwater fittings. (BRCUG)

John Brown, Clydebank, central boiler shop. The Yarrow boiler was described in the *Stoker's Manual* of 1912:

The steam drum runs the whole length of the boiler above the centre of the fire-grate and extends beyond it at the front and back; at each side of the fire-grate there is a water drum. The bottom plate of the steam drum is connected to the top plate of the water drum on each side of the boiler by the generating tubes which are straight, except that rows nearest the fire are bent slightly to it. At the front of the drum outside the boiler casing are two large downcomer tubes connecting the steam drums with the water drums. The feed water is led into the outer sides of the bottom drums, which have a space opposite the top rows of tubes furthest away from the fire baffled off from the rest of the drum. The internal feed pipes are in the space so partitioned off. The whole of the boiler, except the ends of the drums which project, is surrounded by a casing, which is brick-lined and lagged as necessary. The furnace doors, grate-fires, and ash pans are arranged as usual. The gases from the fire are burned in the space above it, mixing with air admitted through a tube in the back casing, and they pass through the tubes on either side reaching the division of the uptake.

(BRCUG)

John Brown, Clydebank, large machine shop, the engine works. (BRCUG)

John Brown, Clydebank, machine shop. (BRCUG)

Parsons, turbine shop. This shop was built by Sir William Arrol and Co., Dalmarnock Iron Works, Glasgow. (BRCUG)

Wallsend Slipway Company, boiler shop. The Babcock and Wilcox boiler was described in the *Stoker's Manual* of 1912:

In this boiler the tubes forming the vertical heating surface are attached to forged steel boxes or headers placed vertically in the boilers. A pair of headers with its connecting tubes form an element. The front headers carry doors through which the tubes, which are placed in zig-zag rows, may be either cleaned or renewed when necessary. The rows of tubes just above the fire and connecting the bottoms of the headers are of larger diameter than the others; these tubes are placed one above the other in the headers, the smaller ones above are placed in pairs side by side. The vertical rows of tubes are staggered to make sure that the gas passes over all tubes, and the headers are similarly bent. Each tube communicates directly with the front and back header, and when elements are in position in the boiler the tubes lie at an angle of 15 degrees with the horizontal. Each front header is connected at the bottom with the feed collector which is a square tube running across the boiler above the furnace doors and at the top with the bottom of the steam collector. Each back header is connected at the top with the steam space of the steam collector by two large tubes. The ends of the steam collector communicate with the downcomers which lead into mud drums, and the water from these returns to the feed collector before going again to the tubes. In this boiler there is a definite water level which is maintained in the steam collector, and each tube is connected to the headers of its element. The headers are placed side by side, forming an airtight wall front and back, between which the flames from the furnaces are directed by baffles over the whole of the tube surface.

(BRCUG)

Beardmore, Dalmuir, cast steel shaft brackets, weight 97 tons. The stern frames, rudders and stem for Dreadnoughts had to be cast individually. (BRCUG)

Beardmore, Dalmuir, patternmakers' shop. It was here that exact wooden replicas were made of equipment that needed to be cast. The patterns were then passed to the foundry where their shapes were replicated in sand moulds ready for casting. (BRCUG)

John Brown, Atlas Works, Sheffield, forging shop. (BRCUG)

John Brown, Atlas Works, Sheffield. After forging, propeller shafts were machined to their required size on long lathes similar to those in the above picture. Thos. Firth and Sons Ltd built the four shafts for HMS *Queen Elizabeth*. Each shaft was 67 ft in length and 17 inches in diameter. (BRCUG)

Armaments

Beardmore, Parkhead, gun factory, a forged tube for 12 inch gun, weight 67 tons. The forging process often took four weeks because the plant was used only intermittently. (BRCUG)

Left: Beardmore, Parkhead, a jacket for a 12 inch gun under a 4,000 ton hydraulic press. The first stage in making a heavy gun was to run the molten metal from the 60 ton furnaces into an octagonal mould. After the ingot had cooled it was placed in a boring mill, where a hole was trepanned through it. The trepanned ingot was reheated until it glowed. It was then put under hydraulic pressure, which squeezed and forged the metal to the desired dimensions. To keep the profile of the bored hole, a hollow mandrel was inserted into the tube. Streams of cold water were passed through the mandrel to cool it as it came into contact with the red-hot gun tube. (BRCUG)

Below: Beardmore, Parkhead, gun factory lathes. When the forging process had been completed the jacket was planed and smoothed by machine tools. A tube forging, which weighed approximately 47 tons for a 12 inch gun, was rough turned on a lathe with a bed of 90–108 ft. Lathes were driven by 40–50 hp independent electric motors and served by 100 ton cranes. These lathes could also be used for large propeller shafts. (BRCUG)

Beardmore, Parkhead, gun factory, hardening (tempering) the tube in oil for a 12 inch gun. The oil bath was sunk vertically into the ground for about 90 ft. It was filled with 126 tons of oil. Above it was the 130 ton Goliath crane, which had a clear lift of 100 ft above the ground. The tube was reheated in the gas-fired furnace. The temperatures were then checked by pyrometers. After this the tube was lifted by the crane and steadily lowered into the oil bath until it was completely immersed. (BRCUG)

Beardmore, Parkhead, gun factory. When the tube was removed from the oil bath, pieces were cut from the ends and examined to make sure that the forging had been satisfactory. (BRCUG)

Beardmore, Parkhead, gun shop. Unlike continental guns, which were hooped, British heavy naval guns were wire wound. The gun's jacket was enveloped in an outer casing of rectangular section steel wire. This was achieved by placing the jacket onto a lathe-type machine, which spun the wire from a large reel of wire on a nearby machine in an endless spiral from one end of the jacket to the other. A contemporary paper presented at the British Association of Science by Mr Douglas Vickers and Lt Dawson RN of the Vickers company stated that 130 miles of wire were wound round the jacket of a 12 inch gun. This increased to 170 miles for a 15 inch gun. The reel carrying the wire was fitted with special gear that maintained a steady tension throughout the winding operation. The tension was varied according to the number of layers. On a 12 inch gun there were approximately ten layers of wound wire. After the tube had been wired it was returned to a lathe, which skimmed off any irregularities in the wire until the exterior of the jacket was symmetrical. (BRCUG)

Beardmore, Parkhead, gun shop, 'one week's output'. Heavy naval guns were more than 60 ft in length and weighed more than 100 tons. They usually took a year to complete. The lengthy routines involved in the making of guns and the accompanying turrets imposed a rigid timetable on Dreadnought construction. (BRCUG)

Beardmore, Parkhead, boring machine for heavy guns. (PCL)

Left: Sir W.G. Armstrong Whitworth and Co. Ltd, Elswick, applying a pressure of 10,000 tons to the tube of a 12 inch gun. Approximately 500 tons of ingots were required to make each forging. Cranes of 200 ton lifting capacity were situated on each side of the hydraulic press and were fitted with special turning gear for revolving the billet while it was being forged under the press. (PCL)

Below: Sir W.G. Armstrong Whitworth and Co. Ltd, Elswick. After the jacketed wire-wound tube had been further hardened, it was returned to the lathe, the operator of which gave the gun a smooth external finish. The wire casing was then measured and an outer casing prepared. This casing was bored at a slightly smaller diameter than the external diameter of the wired tube. The external tube was then heated up and placed over the inner tube. As it cooled, the two tubes became homogenous. The final process was to give the inner surface of the barrel its distinct rifling. (PCL)

Sir W.G. Armstrong Whitworth and Co. Ltd, Elswick, turret erection shop. The shop had to have powerful overhead cranes to cope with the heavy weights involved. Brick pits of about 50 ft in depth were made below floor level. The diameter at the bottom was 15 ft, while the diameter at the top was 40 ft with stairways, electric power and light distribution. The gun turrets were erected in the pits, this involved constructing the plate and angle housing for the guns. This weighed approximately 230 tons and was made of steel plates and bars. Within these were built the training, elevating, hoisting and loading gears, gun wash-out plant, sighting and firing apparatus, electrical and auxiliary pumping machinery, flash-proof doors and interlocking safety devices. Supported on the plate, in addition to the working chamber and trunk, was the main and auxiliary machinery, which weighed about 300 tons. The turntable containing the guns, the machinery and the armoured shield were erected complete in the shop. The turrets usually took between eighteen months and two years to build, although the separate testing of new models could take a further four to six months. If the turret was passed as satisfactory it was then dismantled and taken to the appropriate dockyard or shipyard. (PCL)

Sir W.G. Armstrong Whitworth and Co. Ltd, Elswick. Putting the 13.5 inch guns and turrets onboard HMS *Monarch*. The first lift was put onboard at 2.00 p.m. on 22 July 1911 and the last was completed on 26 July 1911. The total weight of the material handled in four days was 2,800 tons, and the whole operation involved 250 lifts. These were made by a 150 ton crane built in the Elswick Engine Works. (PCL)

The Barr and Stroud factory, Scotstoun, fitting shop for naval rangefinders. (BRCUG)

Vickers, River Don Works, Sheffield, south gun shop. (BRCUG)

Vickers, River Don Works, Sheffield, inspection shop. Final dimensional check before issuing for proof firing. (BRCUG)

Vickers, Barrow-in-Furness, gun erecting shop, 13.5 inch Mark II gun for the battle-cruiser HMS *Princess Royal*. (VSEL)

Vickers, Barrow-in-Furness, gun erecting shop, 15 in gun for the battleship HMS *Revenge*. (VSEL)

Vickers, Barrow-in-Furness, gun mounting department. (PCL)

Vickers, Barrow-in-Furness, 19 November 1915, no. 6 bay in the shell shop. (VSEL)

6: COMMISSIONING, SEA AND GUNNERY TRIALS

No photographs have survived of the commissioning of the Dreadnoughts in the Royal Dockyards, but the John Brown photographic collection does record this with respect to HMS *Barham*, commissioned on 19 August 1915, and HMS *Repulse*, commissioned on 8 August 1916.

'Admiralty Instructions for the Barham's Trials, issued on 30 July 1916, John Brown, Clydebank.

Monday 9th August, 'X' and 'Y' turret crews to join ship.

Tuesday and Wednesday August 10th and 11th, Gunnery equipment trials and hydraulic tests for 'A', 'B', 'X' and 'Y' turrets.

Wednesday 18th August, 10.30 Captain Superintendent's inspection.

Thursday 19th August, All crew to join ship.

Tuesday 24th August, 6 inch ammunition, 40 rounds per gun, to be brought aboard; gunnery equipment and hydraulic tests for 'A' and 'B' turrets.

Wednesday 25th August, gunnery tests for 6 inch guns and further tests in 'A' and 'B' turrets.

Thursday 26th, noon, ship to proceed down river, past survey ship, preliminary trial, return to Tail Bank, then torpedo trials, ship to embark 1,000 tons of oil.

Friday August 27th, HMS *Barham* to steam at 4 hours full power for trials, to carry out 6 inch gun trials, to return to Greenock, to carry out steaming trials, proceed to instructed destination.'

The sea trials usually began with an assessment of the main and auxiliary machinery and the closed exhaust system. Tests were then made running the ship at full power for an hour. There were then analyses of fuel consumption and a 24 hour test, with 12 hours at half power and 12 hours at three-quarters power. A further 4 hour test was made with the ship running at full power. Observations and measurements were made of the ship's water consumption, water feeds and condensers. The bilge pumps were tested. Further engine trials included stopping, starting, reversing and deep load trials. The performance of the auxiliary machinery was carefully monitored. This involved pumping the engines with hydraulic steam and testing the electrical generators, the electrical compressors, the steering gear, the capstans, the refrigerating and ice-making machinery and the electrical generators. The emergency valves in the main steam-pipes were also rigorously tested, as were the feed pipes and the boiler feed valves. Compressed air tests were undertaken and the distilled water of the hydraulic system was examined. There were then further tests for anchorage, and turning trials were undertaken. Those of HMS *Agincourt* were carried out in the North Sea on 22 June 1914. There were full-power and lower-power circle tests. The ship advanced 642 yd while the tests were undertaken at a speed of 20.7 knots. The responsibility for taking the records during the trials lay with the fleet officers and their naval staff. Gangs of dockyard and shipyard workers remained onboard and assisted with the recording of temperatures, the tally of fuel consumption and the recording of water measurements. The Dreadnought was then put through its speed trials. HMS *Repulse*'s trials were carried out on 23 August 1916 using the measured mile on the island of Arran. Ten runs were made, commencing at 125 rpm for the inner shafts, and ending at 269 rpm outer port shaft, 271 rpm for the starboard outer shaft, 253 rpm for the inner port shaft and 281 rpm for the inner starboard shaft. The timed mile speed was recorded at 32.14 knots, which was delivered at 119,250 s.h.p.

The final Dreadnought trials were for the ship's armaments. HMS *Canada*'s were completed on 6 and 7 September 1915 for

'A' and 'B' turrets and 13 September for the 'X' and 'Y' turrets. The report began by stating that, although the guns and machinery were complete as regards loading arrangements, they were not complete in many important details. Schedules outlining in detail the necessary corrective work were handed over to the senior management of W.G. Armstrong and Whitworth Ltd. The gunnery trials for HMS *Queen Elizabeth* were carried out on the equipment on 20, 21, 22, 23, 25 and 29 September 1915. The final report from Capt. Fowler of the naval gunnery school, HMS *Excellent*, contained many critical qualifications.

'It is desired to point out that the tests of Gunnery Equipment of the ship have been seriously hampered by an apparent lack of appreciation of the necessity for the tests on the part of the turret machinery contractors. It was immediately evident in commencing the tests that the representatives of messrs W.G. Armstrong and Whitworth Limited were disposed to adopt the attitude that the preliminary hydraulic trials having already been carried out by Admiralty officers, the testing of equipment by HMS *Excellent* was of no importance. The attitudes reflected in the foremen in charge of the turrets, was the cause of frequent delays, such as pressure not being on the different machines, the ammunition cages not being in adjustment etc., which could have been avoided had a better organization existed for dealing with the defects and necessary adjustments made from the day to day programme of the trials. The result of this lack of organization on the part of the representatives of the hydraulic machinery contractor has been very protracted trials.'

The subsequent report was fifty-five pages in length – the longest of Dreadnought gunnery reports. Its contents were as follows:

I. General remarks on gun trials
II. Programme of firing and remarks
III. Blast
IV. a. General remarks on gunnery equipment
b. Remote and special fittings under trial
c. Criticism of the 15 inch Mark I mounting
V. Its effect for other ships

In the gun houses of 'A' and 'B' turrets the voice pipes were found to be incomplete and there was no branch for transfers to the director and trainer. The voice pipe from the cabinet to the working chamber was incomplete and there should have been a further branch to the officer of quarters. The front guard for the gun layer was found not to be in place, while the front breech lever fouled the floor plates at elevation. The breech cut-off gear required adjustment and the blast excluders were not properly fitted. In the working chamber the interlocking gear between the main hoist and the shell and cordite doors required adjusting. In the shell rooms and magazines the spring on the stop lever was useless as it was fitted too close to the fulcrum, and the stop on the after ends of the rails for the outer and centre runners was badly fitted for preventing the projectiles from running into the bulkhead. Twenty-three faults were itemized for the shell rooms and magazines, and a further nineteen items were outlined for the working chamber. When 'Y' turret was tested it was found that the left cage was adjusted slightly too low, which made it very difficult to load heavy shells into the cage. The automatic teller did not work and it was hard to assess if the tail did not acknowledge that it was 'not ready' when the top of the hoist was reached. The auxiliary cordite cage right door was bent, which meant that the door did not close, the locking gear at the top of the doors was found to be very difficult to work, while the safety lever when the cage was closed did not prevent the cage from being raised. In 'X' turret the engine ran more smoothly to the right than to the left. The left engine became very hot on the rear end bearing and stopped. In general, erection was not good, with regard to both lubrication and bearing. With regard to the criticism of the 15 inch Mark I gun, the report noted that there was a lack of opportunity for continuous loading. The greatest number of rounds loaded was merely seven wooden projectiles and drill cartridges; none of the remaining heavy guns did more than four consecutive loads. A figure of seventy consecutive loads was recommended for an effective assessment. The Gunnery Captain concluded that it was difficult to form any estimate of the effectiveness of the equipment in these conditions.

However, the report's final observation was that many of the difficulties could be remedied easily for future ships because the faults did not result from faulty design. For example, in the gun house the stiffness of the levers on the gun cages was caused by the presence of dirt and the absence of effective lubrication. Most of the faults related to incorrect fitting and adjustment. Some flaws did remain, as with the steps on the back of the gun loading cage, which received heavy blows every time a projectile was rammed into the gun-loading cage in the working chamber, despite the buffer. These gunnery reports varied from ship to ship for, while the HMS *Queen Elizabeth* report amounted to fifty-five pages, the report for the sister ship HMS *Warspite*, whose gunnery trials were completed on 12, 13 and 15 August 1915, was only twenty-two pages. The reason for this was that HMS *Queen Elizabeth*, as a prototype, had the first 15 inch guns, which obviously had to be thoroughly tested.

John Brown, Clydebank, HMS *Barham*, 25 August 1915, one of the Queen
Elizabeth class battleships. These were the first 15 inch gun battleships, the

first oil-fired battleships and the first to steam over 24 knots. They are considered to be the finest product of the Dreadnought period. (BRCUG)

John Brown, Clydebank, HMS *Barham*, 25 August 1915, ship's commissioning. The 6 inch casemates under 'Y' turret were never fitted. Only the *Queen Elizabeth* was completed with the after 6 inch guns, which were removed later. To compensate, a singular 6 inch gun in an open gun-house was mounted each side amidships in all of the class.

John Brown, Clydebank, HMS *Repulse*, 12 August 1916, ship's commissioning. (BRCUG)

Overleaf: top: Profile of HMS *Hood* at speed, undated. Torpedo trials were carried out on 23 February and 3 March 1920. Steam and gunnery trials occurred throughout March. With a displacement of 42,200 tons with 1,200 tons of oil on board, HMS *Hood* recorded 151,280 s.h.p. and achieved 32.07 knots at 207 rpm. With a displacement of 44,600 tons, 150,220 s.h.p. was recorded for a mean speed of 31.9 knots at 204 rpm. On completion of the trials, careful examinations of the hull were carried out in Rosyth Dockyard. (BRCUG). *Bottom:* HMS *Repulse*, 23 August 1916, measured mile trial. The *Admiralty Steam Manual* of 1910 listed the following trials: Preliminary Trial, Contractors' Trials, Commissioning Trial, Turning Trials, Special Measured Mile Trial. The ship left Clydebank and arrived at the Tail of the Bank, Firth of Clyde, at 3.00 p.m. (BRCUG)

Arran Course Trials:

Displacement: 28,202 tons
Draught: 26 ft 2 inch forward, 27 ft 7 inch aft
Diameter of propellers: 13 ft 6 inch

Mean rpm: 273.5
Mean s.h.p.: 116,992
Speed: 31.31 knots

HMS *Hood* leaving Clydebank, 9 July 1920. John Brown had received permission from the Admiralty to let the almost complete battle-cruiser leave the fitting-out basin to allow the firm to complete various merchant vessels. Some preliminary trials occurred in the Firth of Clyde while the ship was en route for Rosyth Dockyard. On this trip the

ship encountered a force 8 wind from the west, which soon showed that HMS *Hood* was a wet ship. This was partly caused by the additional armour added to the ship during the course of its construction. It was estimated that deep load for HMS *Hood* was 46,680 tons, some 2.7 per cent heavier than the original selected design. (BRCUG)

Fitting-out basin, Vickers, Barrow-in-Furness, HMS *Princess Royal* and the Japanese battle-cruiser *Kongo*. (VSEL)

Portsmouth Dockyard, HMS *Dreadnought* entering 15 dock; HMS *Bellerophon* can be seen fitting-out on

the left of the picture. (PCL)

7: EPILOGUE

To imagine a battle between two great modern iron-clad ships, you must not think of . . . two men in armour striking at each other with heavy swords. It is more like a battle between two egg shells striking each other with hammers.

Winston Churchill, First Lord of the Admiralty, House of Commons, 1912

The complex issues of naval policy and doctrine associated with the Dreadnought programme and its strategic assumptions have occupied naval historians and students of policy to a remarkable extent, and their deliberations have yielded a formidable historiography, which is still unfolding.

Always controversial, the debate got into its stride in the modern period with the work of Arthur Marder, whose magisterial writing on the subject is contained in the volumes entitled *From the Dreadnought to Scapa Flow: the Royal Navy in the Fisher Era* (London, Oxford Unversity Press, 1961–1970, vol. 1) and *The Road to War, 1904–1915*. The latter is particularly relevant to the above discussion. More recently, Jon Sumida, in his *Defence of Naval Supremacy: Finance, Technology and British Naval Policy, 1889–1913* (London, Unwin Hyman, 1989), has drawn attention to the problems of fire control in the Dreadnoughts, which did not adopt the superior Pollen system until after the Battle of Jutland. Sumida has also set out the case for reassessing several of Marder's assumptions concerning Fisher's services as First Sea Lord, in particular his attitude towards ship design and naval strategy. The extent to which naval affairs impinged on British politics and their part in the events that led to the First World War has been admirably covered by Paul Kennedy in *The Rise of Anglo-German Antagonism, 1860–1914* (London, Allen and Unwin, 1980) and R.J. Morris *The Scaremongers: the Advocacy of War and Re-armament* (London, Routledge, Kegan and Paul, 1984). With regard to Dreadnought design and technical specifications, R.A. Burt, John Roberts and Ross Watton have undertaken thorough appraisals of the technological and operational histories of the early Dreadnoughts and later Super-Dreadnoughts. Their books, listed below, also contain selections of photographs of completed Dreadnoughts, both battleships and battle-cruisers, and Roberts' books contain outstanding sectional ship drawings.

While Hugh Lyon, in his paper on 'The Admiralty and private industry' (in *Technical Change and British Naval Policy*, ed. Brian Ranft, London), looks at the often fraught relationship between the Admiralty and private industry, including the shipbuilders and the armament manufacturers, Hugh B. Peebles, in the early chapters of his *Warshipbuilding on the Clyde: Naval Orders and the Prosperity of the Clyde Shipbuilding Industry, 1889–1939* (Edinburgh, John Donald, 1989), shows the significant part played by the Scottish shipbuilders in the Dreadnought years and looks at the impact on the industry of fluctuating demand for warships. Finally, in a new challenging work by Andrew Gordon, *The Rules of the Game: Jutland and British Naval Command* (London, John Murray, 1996), the encounter between Jellicoe's Grand Fleet and the German High Seas Fleet of Admiral Scheer is put under a particularly sharp and searching scrutiny.

Who won and lost the action remained for a long time in dispute. Admiral Scheer, relieved to have got away with the loss of one Dreadnought and the sacrifice of some 2,500 men, claimed a victory, at least in numerical terms, over the Grand Fleet, which lost three Dreadnoughts and some 6,000 men. In material terms, Scheer sunk 115,000 tons against the loss of some 60,000 tons, yet scholarship inclines to the view that Jellicoe's actions won the day for Britain, in effect successfully deterring the Germans from making any further, large fleet sorties and securing the position of the Royal Navy in the North Sea as the dominant sea power. The extraordinarily complicated progress of the battle, as Andrew Gordon demonstrated, conceals a more interesting subplot, embracing strategic confusion, tactical errors and operational misjudgements that, added to muddled objectives and clashes of personality, have helped to keep the Jutland controversy bubbling away.

This book has sought to demonstrate, chiefly by visual means, something of the scale of the effort that went into constructing the British Dreadnought battlefleet. The financial expenditure, the hard work and long hours of overtime, by a highly skilled and determined shipbuilding labour force in both the Royal Dockyards and in the commercial shipyards, and the huge quantities of materials consumed have all been touched on, although we have not examined the, at times frenzied, political debate that characterized the period and the sacrifice of other political aims – in the fields of education, social warfare, housing reform – to the Naval vote. The Dreadnought programme had worked up the expectations of the public to an almost impossible degree, and it is fairly clear that the British embarked on the Naval war in 1914 expecting to win it simply by fighting another Trafalgar. Hence the sense of disappointment that swept the country in the aftermath of Jutland: so much had been promised; so little, it seemed, had been delivered. Of course, the Royal Navy did indeed help to win the war, but it was by the unseen, and to some extent unsung, blockade of Germany, and by the defeat of the U-boat in the North Atlantic, that victory was in due time to be achieved. For after Jutland the Germans turned to the submarine in their quest for maritime superiority.

Thus, while the nation's pride, the mighty Grand Fleet, lay fretting at anchor in Scapa Flow, seething with disappointment at its failure to achieve a decisive result in the sole encounter with the High Seas Fleet, it was the relatively enfeebled portion of the Royal Navy dedicated to anti-submarine warfare, neglected in the push for Dreadnought supremacy, that had to carry the fight to the enemy. Battleships, battle-cruisers and the large armoured cruisers on which naval construction had concentrated, were ineffective against the new enemy. The rules of the game had changed and things would never be quite the same again.

ALPHABETICAL LIST OF DREADNOUGHTS

Agincourt
Ajax
Audacious
Australia

Barham
Bellerophon
Benbow

Canada
Centurion
Colossus
Collingwood
Conqueror
Courageous

Dreadnought

Emperor of India
Erin

Furious

Glorious

Hercules
Hood

Iron Duke
Indefatigable
Indomitable
Inflexible
Invincible

King George V

Lion

Malaya
Marlborough
Monarch

Neptune
New Zealand

Orion

Princess Royal

Queen Elizabeth
Queen Mary

Ramillies
Renown
Repulse
Resolution
Revenge
Royal Oak
Royal Sovereign

St Vincent
Superb

Temeraire
Thunderer
Tiger

Valiant
Vanguard

Warspite

APPENDIX

[All details of ships are as on completion from the builders.]

BRITISH BATTLESHIPS

DREADNOUGHT (Battleship, 1905 Programme)

Ship	Built at	Laid down	Launched	Completed
Dreadnought	Portsmouth	02/10/05	10/02/06	Dec. 1906
Dimensions	527'×82'×26.5'			
Displacement	17,900 tons	21,845 tons deep load		
Armament	10×12"	27×12 pdr	18" torpedo tubes	
Protection	Belt 11"–8"–6"–4"	Bulkheads 8"	Barbettes 11"–4"	Turrets 11"	Control Tower 11"
Machinery	Parsons turbines 23,000 hp	21 knots	4 screws	18 Babcock & Wilcox boilers
Fuel	2,900 tons coal	1,120 tons oil		
Radius	6,620 at 10 knots	4,910 at 18 knots		
Complement	773			
Fate	Sold March 1921, broken up at Inverkeithing 1923.			

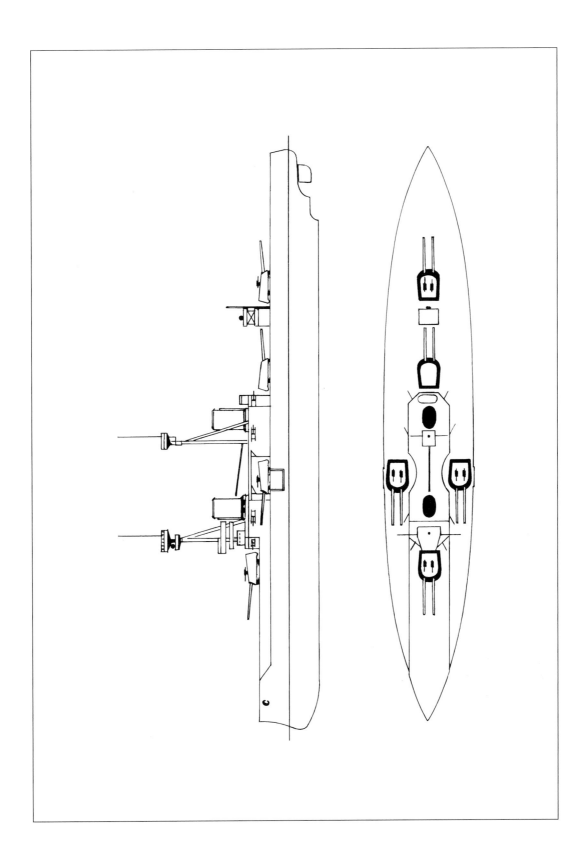

ST VINCENT Class (Battleship, 1907 Programme)

Ship	Built at	Laid down	launched	Completed
St Vincent	Portsmouth	30/12/07	10/09/08	May 1909
Collingwood	Devonport	03/02/08	07/11/08	Apr. 1910
Vanguard	Vickers	02/04/08	22/02/09	Feb. 1910

Dimensions 536'×84'×25.25'

Displacement 19,250 tons 23,030 deep load

Armament 10×12" 20×4" 4×3 pdr 5×18" torpedo tubes

Protection Belt 10"–7" Bulkheads 8"–4" Barbettes 9"–5" Turrets 11" Conning Tower 11"–8"

Machinery Parsons turbines 24,500 hp 21 knots 4 screws

Fuel 2,800 tons coal 940 tons oil

Radius 6,900 at 10 knots 4,250 at 18.7 knots

Complement 758

Fate
St Vincent Discarded under the Washington Treaty 1 December 1921 and broken up at Dover.
Collingwood Discarded under the Washington Treaty 12 December 1922 and broken up at Newport.
Vanguard Destroyed by internal explosion at Scapa Flow 9 July 1917, 804 men perished.

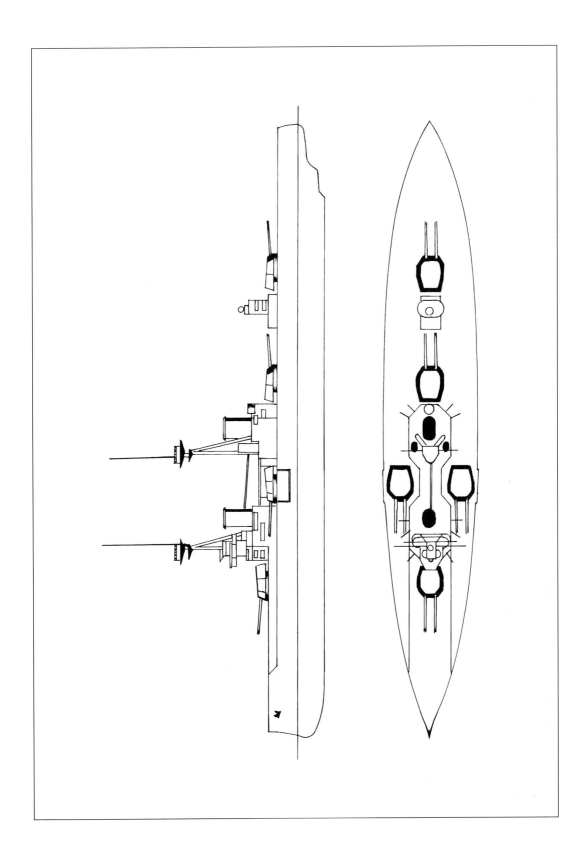

NEPTUNE (Battleship, 1908 Programme)

Ship	Built at	Laid down	Launched	Completed
Neptune	Portsmouth	19/01/09	30/09/09	Jan. 11
Dimensions	546'×85'×24'			
Displacement	19,680 tons	22,720 deep load		
Armament	10×12"	16×4"	4×3 pdr	2×18" beam & 1×18" stern torpedo tubes
Protection	Belt 10"–7"	Bulkheads 8"–4"	Barbettes 9"–5"	Turrets 11"	Conning Tower 11"
Machinery	Parsons turbines 25,000 hp	21 knots	4 screws	Yarrow boilers
Fuel	2,710 tons coal	790 tons oil		
Radius	6,330 at 10 knots	3,820 at 18.5 knots		
Complement	759			
Fate	Discarded under the Washington Treaty 1 September 1922 and broken up at Blyth.			

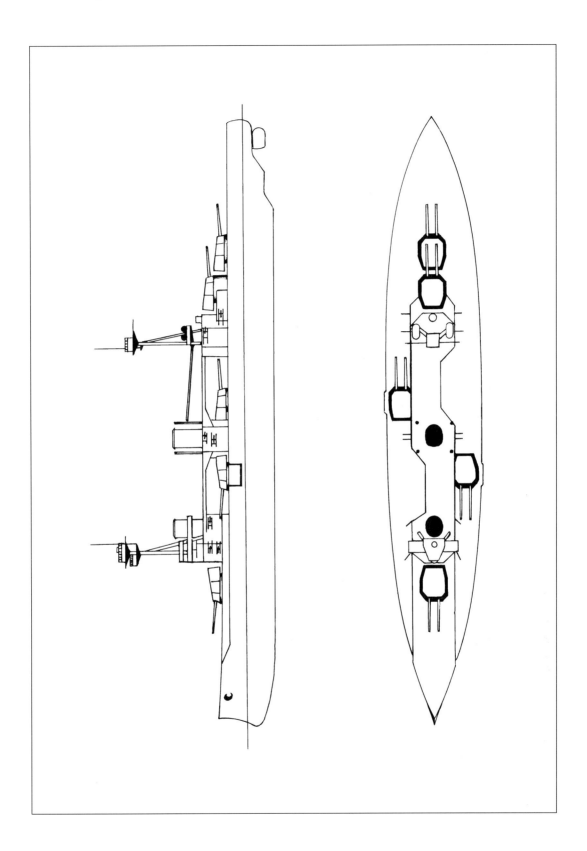

INDEFATIGABLE Class (Battlecruiser, 1908 Programme)

Ship	Built at	Laid down	Launched	Completed
Indefatigable	Devonport	25/02/09	28/10/09	Feb. 1911
Australia	John Brown & Co	23/06/10	25/10/11	Jun. 1913
New Zealand	Fairfield	20/06/10	01/07/11	Nov. 1912

Dimensions 590'×80'×24.75'

Displacement 18,800 tons   22,080 deep load

Armament 8×12"   16×4"   4×3 pdr   2×18" torpedo tubes

Protection Belt 6"–5"   Bulkheads 4"   Barbettes 7"–4"   Turrets 7"   Conning Tower 10"

Machinery 44,000 hp   25 knots   4 screws   31 Babcock & Wilcox boilers

Fuel 3,170 tons coal   840 tons oil

Radius 6,330 at 10 knots   2,290 at 23.5 knots

Complement 800

Fate

Indefatigable Destroyed by magazine explosion during gun duel with *Von der Tann*, Jutland, 31 May 1915, 1605 hrs, 1,017 men lost.

Australia Discarded under the Washington Treaty and sunk off Sydney harbour, 1924.

New Zealand Discarded under the Washington Treaty and broken up in Germany, 1922.

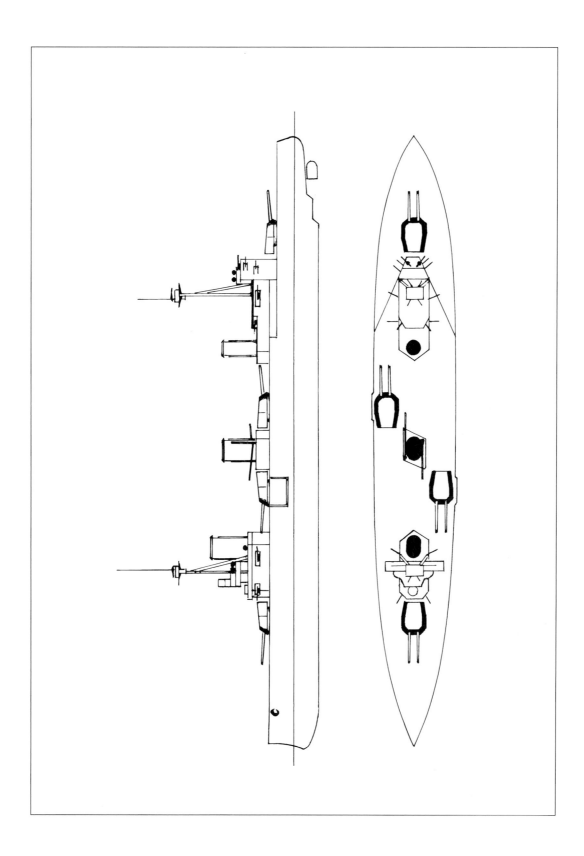

COLOSSUS Class (Battleship, 1909 Programme)

Ship	Built at	Laid down	Launched	Completed
Colossus	Scotts	08/07/09	09/04/10	Jul. 1911
Hercules	Palmers	30/07/09	10/05/10	Aug. 1911
Dimensions	546'×85'×25.25'			
Displacement	20,000 tons	23,050 tons deep load		
Armament	10×12" 16×4"	4×3 pdr	2×21" beam & 1×18" stern torpedo tubes	
Protection	Belt 11"–8"–7" Bulkheads 10"–8"–5"–4" Barbettes 11" down to 4" Turrets 11" Conning Tower 11"			
Machinery	Parsons turbines 25,000 hp 21 knots 4 screws 18 Yarrow or Babcock boilers			
Fuel	2,900 tons coal	800 tons oil		
Radius	6,680 at 10 knots	4,050 at 18.5 knots		
Complement	755			
Fate	*Colossus*	Discarded under the Washington Treaty and broken up at Alloa, 1922.		
	Hercules	Discarded under the Washington Treaty 8 November 1921 and broken up at Kiel.		

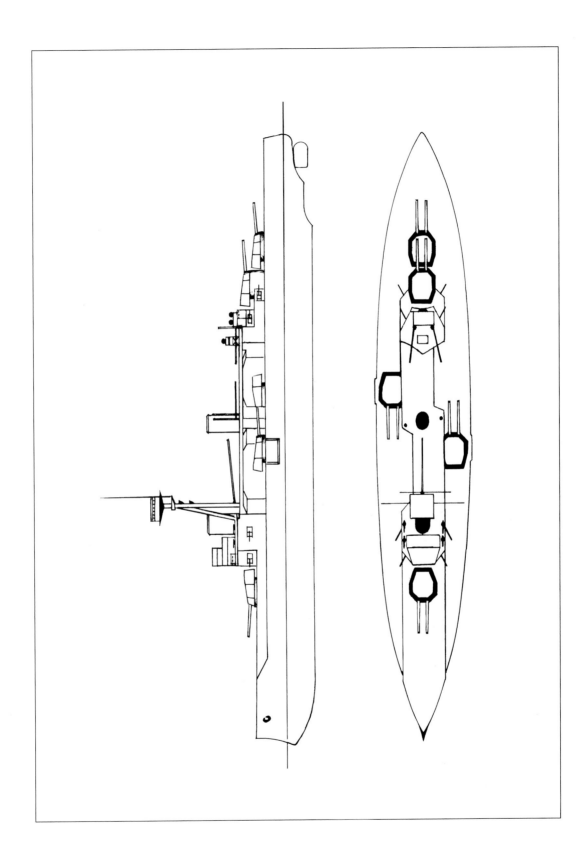

ORION Class (Battleship, 1909 Programme)

Ship	Built at	Laid down	Launched	Completed
Orion	Portsmouth	29/11/09	20/08/10	Jan. 1912
Monarch	Armstrong	01/04/10	30/03/11	Mar. 1912
Conqueror	Beardsmore	05/04/10	01/05/11	Nov. 1912
Thunderer	Thames Iron Works	13/04/10	01/02/11	June 1912

Dimensions 581'×88.5'×24.9'

Displacement 22,500 tons 25,870 tons deep load

Armament 10×13.5" 16×4" 4×3 pdr 2×21" beam & 1×18" stern torpedo tubes

Protection Belt 12"–9"–8" Bulkheads 10"–8"–3" Barbettes 10"–7"–6" Turrets 11" Conning Tower 11"

Machinery Turbines 27,000 hp 21 knots 4 screws 18 Babcock & Yarrow boilers

Fuel 3,300 tons coal 800 tons oil

Radius 6,730 at 10 knots 4,110 at 19 knots

Complement 752

Fate

Orion Discarded under the Washington Treaty 19 December 1922 and broken up at Upnor.

Monarch Sunk as fleet target by *Revenge* off Scilly Islands, 20 January 1925.

Conqueror Discarded under the Washington Treaty 19 December 1922 and broken up at Upnor.

Thunderer Sold 10 December 1926, ran aground en route to Blyth for breaking up, 1927.

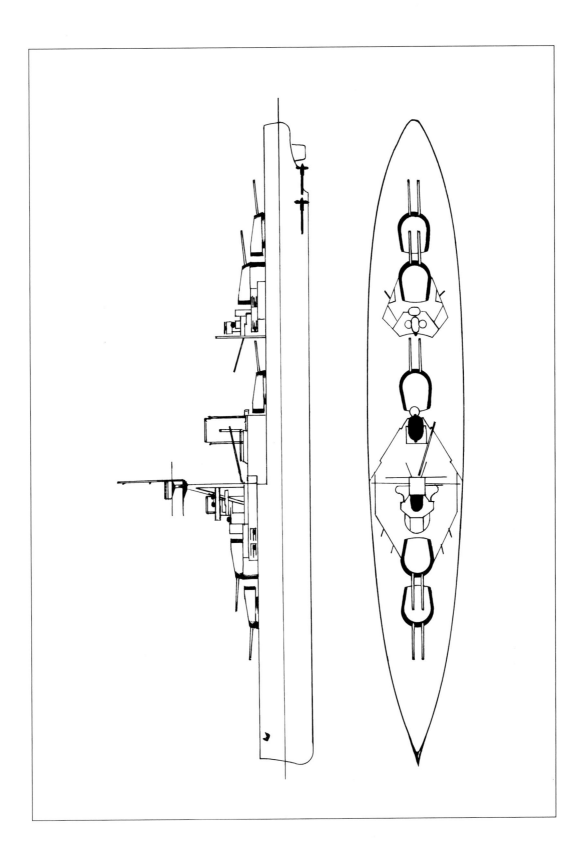

LION Class (Battlecruiser, 1909–10 Programme)

Ship	Built at	Laid down	Launched	Completed
Lion	Devonport	29/11/09	06/08/10	May 1912
Princess Royal	Vickers	02/05/10	29/04/11	Nov. 1912
Queen Mary	Palmers	06/03/11	20/03/12	Sep. 1912

Dimensions 700'×88.5'×26.4'

Displacement 26,270 tons   29,680 tons deep load

Armament 8×13.5"   16×4"   4×3 pdr   2×21" torpedo tubes

Protection Belt 9"–6"–4"   Bulkheads 4"   Barbettes 9"–6"–4"–3"   Turrets 9"   Conning Tower 10"

Machinery Parsons s.h.p. 70,000   27 knots   4 screws   42 Yarrow boilers

Fuel 3,500 tons coal   1,135 tons oil

Radius 5,610 at 10 knots   2,420 at 23.9 knots

Complement 997

Fate

Lion Discarded under the Washington Treaty, sold January 1924 and broken up at Jarrow.

Princess Royal Discarded under the Washington Treaty 1922, sold and broken up at Rosyth 1926.

Queen Mary Destroyed by magazine explosion after direct hits from German battlecruisers, 31 May 1916, 1626 hrs, 1,266 men perished.

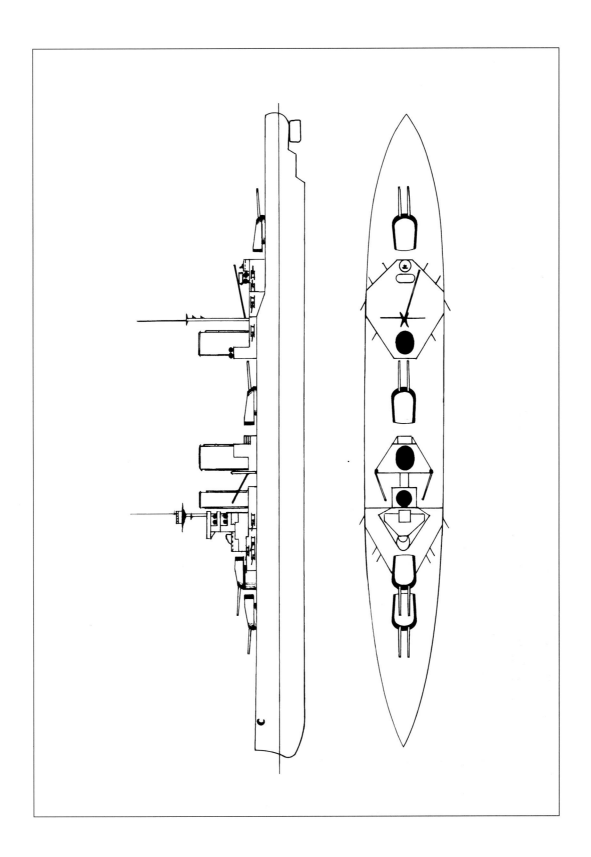

KING GEORGE V Class (Battleship, 1910 Programme)

Ship	Built at	Laid down	Launched	Completed
King George V	Portsmouth	16/01/11	09/10/11	Nov. 1912
Ajax	Scotts	27/02/11	21/03/12	Mar. 1912
Audacious	Lairds	23/03/11	14/09/12	Oct. 1912
Centurion	Devonport	16/01/11	18/11/11	May 1913

Dimensions 597.5'×89'×26.6'

Displacement 23,000 tons 25,700 deep load

Armament 10×13.5" 16×4" 4×3 pdr 3×21" torpedo tubes

Protection Belt 12"–9"–8" Bulkheads 10"–6"–4"- Barbettes 10" Turrets 11" Conning Tower 11"

Machinery Parsons turbines 31,000 hp 21.7 knots 4 screws

Fuel 3,150 tons coal 800 tons oil

Radius 4,060 at 18.15 knots

Complement 782

Fate

King George V Sold December 1926 and broken up at Rosyth.
Ajax Sold November 1926 and broken up at Rosyth.
Audacious Sunk by mine near Lough Swilly, 27 October 1914.
Centurion Sunk as block ship after Normandy landing, 9 June 1944.

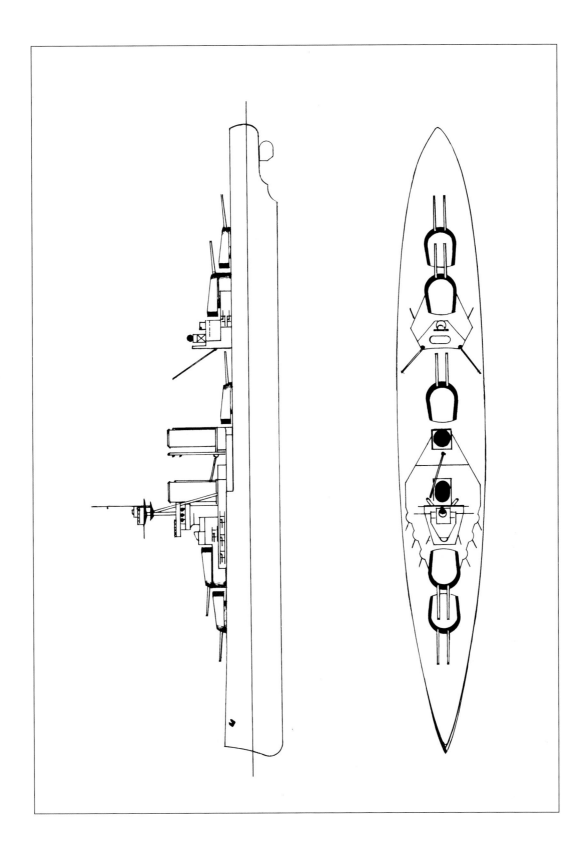

IRON DUKE Class (Battleship, 1911 Programme)

Ship	Built at	Laid down	Launched	Completed
Iron Duke	Portsmouth	12/01/12	12/10/12	Mar. 1914
Marlborough	Devonport	25/01/12	24/10/12	June 1914
Benbow	Beardmore	30/05/12	12/11/13	Oct. 1914
Emperor of India	Vickers	31/05/12	27/11/13	Nov. 1914

Dimensions 622.75'×90'×27.4'

Displacement 25,000 tons   30,380 tons deep load

Armament 10×13.5"   12×6"   2×3"   4×3 pdr   4 × 21" torpedo tubes

Protection Belt 12"–9"–8"–6"–4"   Bulkheads 8"–6"–4"   Barbettes 10"–3"   Turrets 11"   Conning Tower 11"

Machinery Parsons turbines s.h.p. 29,000   21.25 knots   4 screws   18 boilers

Fuel 3,250 tons coal   1,600 tons oil

Radius 4,840 at 19 knots   7,780 at 20.4 knots

Complement 995

Fate

Iron Duke Reduced under the terms of the Washington Treaty. Sold for breaking up at Faslane 2 March 1946.
Marlborough Reduced under the terms of the Washington Treaty. Sold for breaking up at Rosyth 27 June 1932.
Benbow Reduced under the terms of the Washington Treaty. Sold for breaking up at Rosyth, January 1931.
Emperor of India Reduced under the terms of the Washington Treaty. Sunk as target off Owers Bank, 1 July 1931, raised and broken up at Rosyth, December 1931.

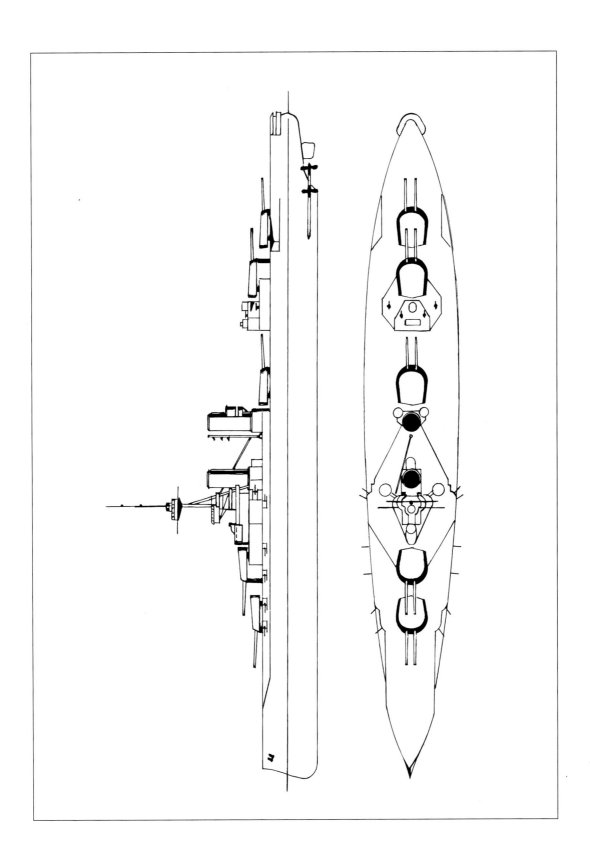

TIGER (Battlecruiser, 1911 Programme)

Ship	Built at	Laid down	Launched	Completed
Tiger	Browns & Co	20/06/12	15/12/13	Oct. 1914
Dimensions	704'×90.5'×28.4'			
Displacement	28,430 tons	35,160 tons deep load		
Armament	8×13.5" 12×6" 4×3 pdr 4×21" torpedo tubes			
Protection	Belt 9"–6"–5"–4"–3" Bulkheads 4"–2" Barbettes 9"–8"–4" Turrets 9" Conning Tower 10"–3"			
Machinery	Brown-Curtis Turbines s.h.p. 108,000 29 knots 4 screws 39 Babcock & Wilcox boilers			
Fuel	3,480 tons coal 450 tons oil			
Radius	5,700 at 12 knots			
Complement	1,121			
Fate	*Tiger* Sold February 1932 and broken up at Inverkeithing.			

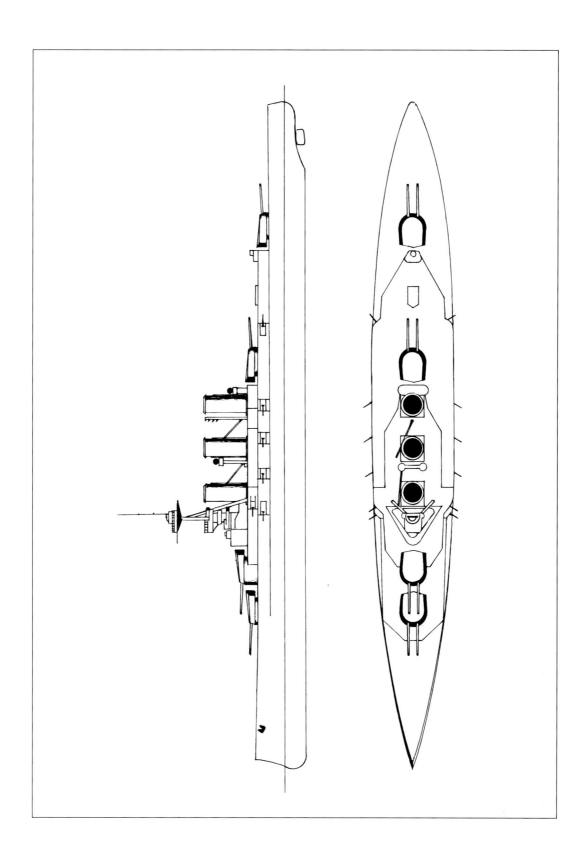

QUEEN ELIZABETH Class (Battleship, 1912 Programme)

Ship	Built at	Laid down	Launched	Completed
Queen Elizabeth	Portsmouth	21/10/12	16/10/13	Jan. 1915
Barham	John Brown & Co.	24/02/13	31/10/14	Oct. 1915
Malaya	Armstrongs	20/10/13	18/03/15	Feb. 1916
Valiant	Fairfield	31/01/13	04/11/14	Feb. 1916
Warspite	Devonport	31/10/12	26/11/13	Mar. 1916

Dimensions 654.75'×90.5'×29.6'

Displacement 27,500 tons   33,000 tons deep load

Armament 8×15"   14×6"   2×3"   4×3 pdr   4×21" torpedo tubes

Protection Belt 13"–6"   Bulkheads 6"–4"   Barbettes 10"–4"   Turrets 13"   Conning Tower 11"

Machinery Turbines 75,000 hp   24 knots   4 screws   24 boilers

Fuel 100 tons coal   3,400 tons oil

Radius 6,540 at 10 knots

Complement 951

Fate

Queen Elizabeth — Sold June 1948 and broken up at Dalmuir & Troon.

Barham — 25 November 1941 when on patrol between Crete and Cyrenaica she was struck by three torpedoes from U-331, capsized and blew up with the loss of 862 men.

Malaya — Sold April 1948 and broken up at Faslane.

Valiant — Sold March 1948 and broken up at Cairnryan & Troon.

Warspite — Ran aground at Prussia Cove, Cornwall, while under tow to the shipbreakers, 23 April 1947, broken on site.

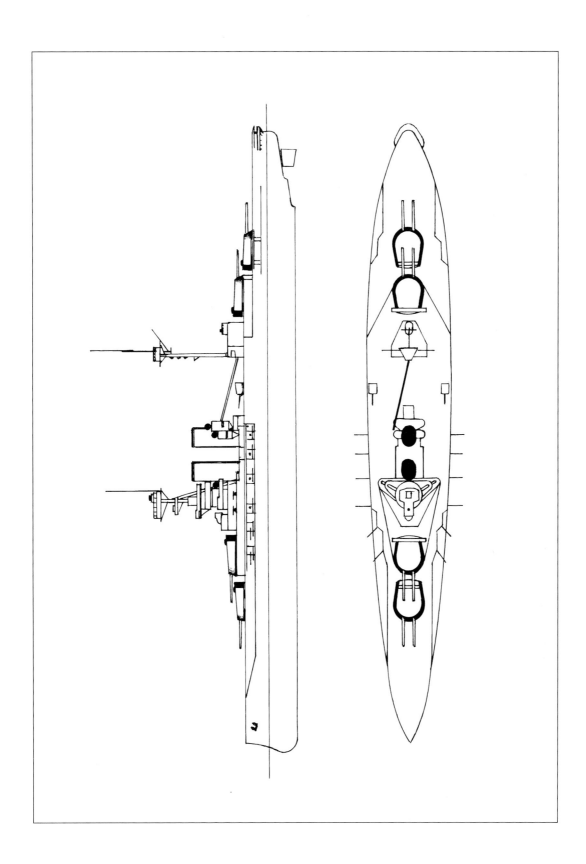

ROYAL SOVEREIGN Class (Battleship, 1913 Programme)

Ship	Built at	Laid Down	Launched	Completed
Ramillies	Beardmore	12/11/13	12/09/16	Sep. 1917
Resolution	Palmers	29/12/13	14/01/15	Dec. 1916
Revenge	Vickers	22/12/13	29/05/15	Mar. 1916
Royal Oak	Devonport	15/01/14	17/11/14	May 1916
Royal Sovereign	Portsmouth	15/01/14	29/11/15	May 1916

Dimensions 624.25'×88.5'×28.6'

Displacement 27,500 tons   31,200 tons deep load

Armament 8×15"   14×6"   2×3"   4×3 pdr   4×21" torpedo tubes

Protection Belt 13"–6"–4"   Bulkheads 6"–4"   Barbettes 10"–9"–7"–6"–4"   Turrets 13"   Conning Tower 11"

Machinery Parsons s.h.p. 40,000   23 knots   4 screws   18 Babcock & Wilcox or Yarrow boilers

Fuel 140 tons coal   3,400 tons oil

Radius 6,800 at 10 knots

Complement 997

Fate

Ramillies Sold April 1948 and broken up at Cairnryan.

Resolution Sold May 1948 and broken up at Faslane.

Revenge Sold March 1949 and broken up at Inverkeithing.

Royal Oak Struck by four torpedoes from U-47 in Scapa flow, capsized and sank within ten minutes with the loss of 833 men, 14 October 1939.

Royal Sovereign Sold April 1949 and broken up at Inverkeithing.

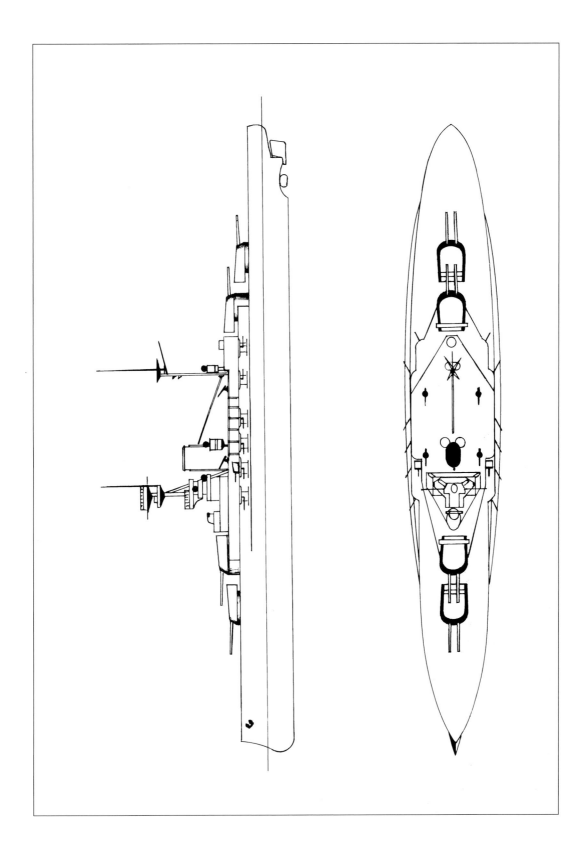

ERIN (Battleship, War Purchase)

Ship	Built at	Laid down	Launched	Completed
Erin	Vickers	01/08/11	03/09/13	Aug. 1914
Dimensions	559.5'×91.6'×28.8'			
Displacement	23,000 tons	25,250 tons deep load		
Armament	10×13.5"	16×6"	6×6 pdr	4×12" torpedo tubes
Protection	Belt 12"–9"–8"–6"–4"	Bulkheads 8"–5"–4"	Barbettes 10"–9"–5"–3"	Turrets 11"	Conning Tower 12"–4"
Machinery	Parsons made by Vickers s.h.p. 26,500 21 knots 4 screws 15 Babcock & Wilcox boilers			
Fuel	2,120 tons coal	710 tons oil		
Radius	5,300 at 10 knots			
Complement	1,070			
Fate	*Erin*	Originally built for Turkey and launched as *Reshadieh*, seized by the British government August 1914 and re-named *Erin*. Discarded under the Washington Treaty 1921. Sold and broken up at Queenborough, December 1922.		

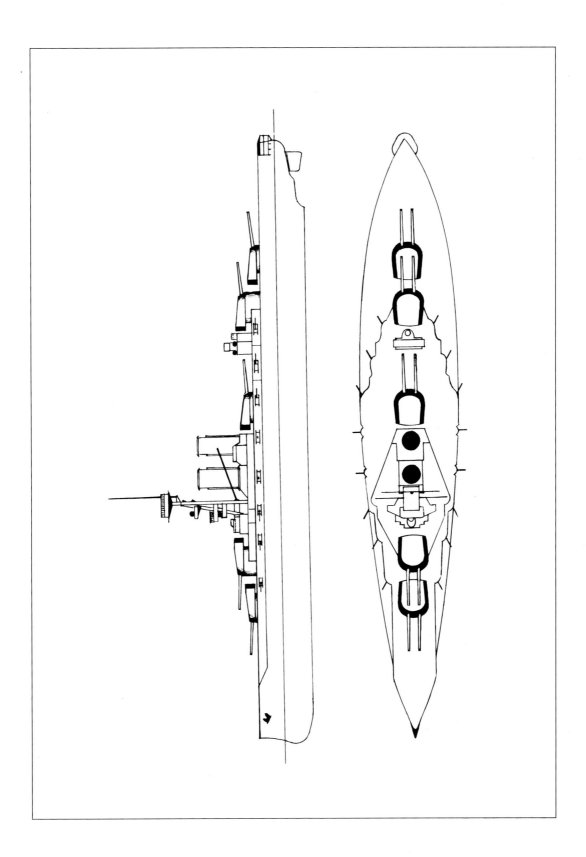

AGINCOURT (Battleship, War Purchase)

Ship	Built at	Laid down	Launched	Completed
Agincourt	Elswick	14/09/11	22/01/13	Aug. 1914
Dimensions	671.5'×89'×27'			
Displacement	27,500 tons	30,250 tons deep load		
Armament	14×12" 20×6" 10×3" 3×21" torpedo tubes			
Protection	Belt 9"–6"–4" Bulkheads 6"–3" Barbettes 9"–3" Turrets 12" Conning Tower 12"			
Machinery	Parsons s.h.p. 34,000 22 knots 4 screws 22 Babcock & Wilcock boilers			
Fuel	3,200 tons coal	620 tons oil		
Radius	4,000 at 10 knots			
Complement	1,115			
Fate	*Agincourt*	Originally laid down as *Rio de Janeiro* for Brazil. Sold to Turkey 9 January 1914, re-named *Sultan Osman I.* Seized by British government 2 August 1914 and re-named *Agincourt*. Discarded under the terms of the Washington Treaty 1921 and broken up at Rosyth.		

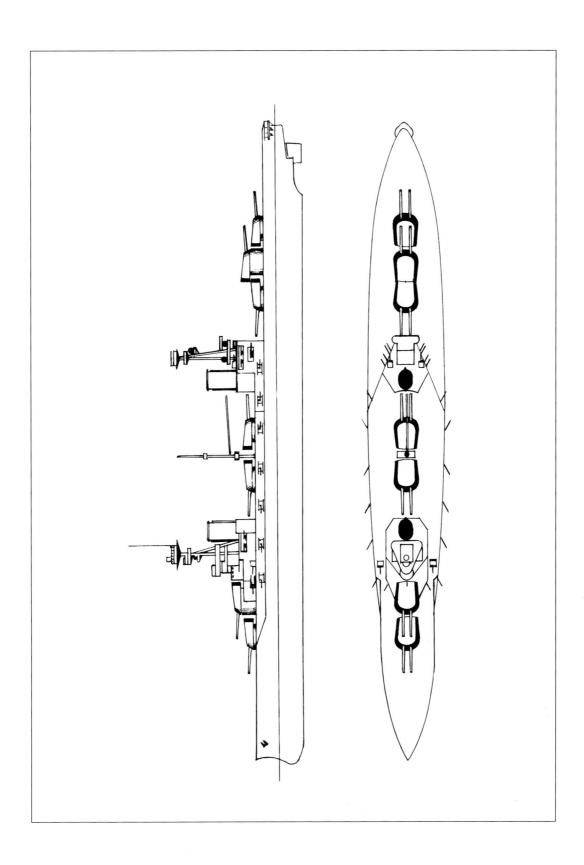

CANADA (Battleship, War Purchase)

Ship	Built at	Laid down	Launched	Completed
Canada	Elswick	27/11/11	27/11/13	Sep. 1915

Dimensions	661'×92'×29'
Displacement	28,600 tons 32,120 tons deep load
Armament	10×14" 16×6" 2×3" 4×3 pdr 4×21" torpedo tubes
Protection	Belt 9"–4" Bulkheads 4.5"–3" Barbettes 10"–4" Turrets 10" Conning Tower 11"–6"
Machinery	Brown-Curtis (HP) and Parsons (LP) turbines s.h.p. 37,000 22.5 knots 4 screws 21 Yarrow boilers
Fuel	3,300 tons coal 520 tons oil
Radius	4,400 at 10 knots
Complement	1,167
Fate	*Canada* One of two battleships built for Chile. Launched as *Almirante Latorre*. 9 September 1914 purchased by British government and re-named *Canada*. 1 August 1920 returned to Chile as *Almirante Latorre*. Discarded 1958 and broken up in Yokohama 1959. Sister ship *Almirante Cochrane* purchased by British government in 1917 for conversion to aircraft carrier and re-named *Eagle*. Torpedoed and sunk on Malta convoy ('Operation Pedestal'), 11 August 1942.

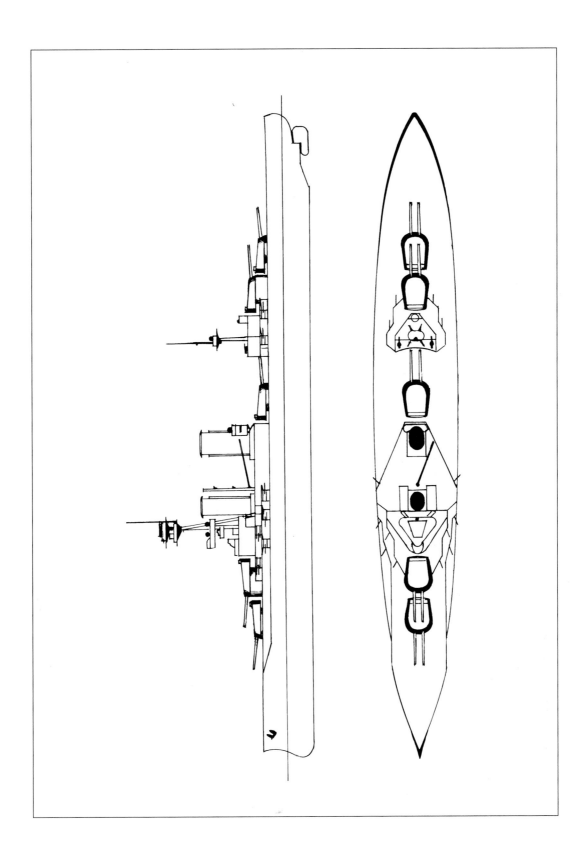

RENOWN Class (Battlecruiser, Emergency War Programme)

Ship	Built at	Laid down	Launched	Completed
Renown	Fairfield & Co.	25/01/15	04/03/16	20/09/16
Repulse	John Brown & Co.	25/01/15	08/01/16	18/08/16

Dimensions 794'×90'×25.7'

Displacement 26,500 tons   32,727 tons deep load

Armament 6×15"   17×4"   2×3"   4×3 pdr   2×21" torpedo tubes

Protection Belt 6"–4"–3"–1.5"   Bulkheads 4"–3"   Barbettes 7"–5"–4"   Turrets 11"–7"   Conning Tower 10"

Machinery Brown & Curtis turbines s.h.p. 112,000   32.6 knots   4 screws   42 Babcock & Wilcox boilers

Fuel 4,243 tons oil

Radius 4,200 at 10 knots

Complement 967

Fate

Renown Sold and broken up at Faslane, 19 March 1948.

Repulse Bombed and torpedoed by Japanese aircraft off the east coast of Malaya, 10 December 1941; sank with the loss of 327 men.

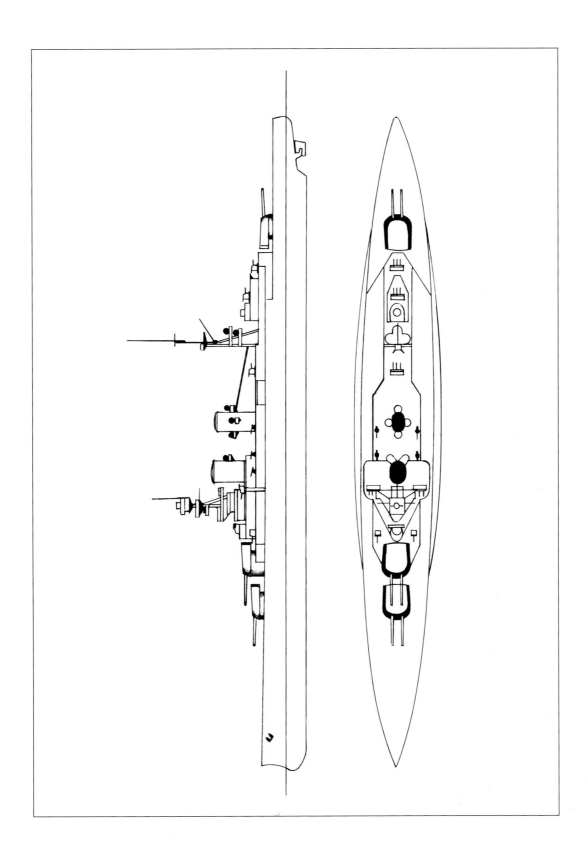

COURAGEOUS, GLORIOUS & FURIOUS (Emergency War Programme)

Ship	Built at	Laid down	Launched	Completed
Courageous	Elswick	28/03/15	05/02/16	Jan. 1917
Glorious	Harland & Wolf	01/05/15	20/04/16	Jan. 1917
Furious	Elswick	08/06/15	15/08/16	Jul. 1917

Dimensions
Furious 786'×81'×23.4'
786.5'×88'×19.75'

Displacement 18,600 tons
Furious 19,513 tons
22,690 tons deep load
22,890 tons deep load

Armament 4×15" 2×3"
Furious 2×18" designed 11×5.5" 2×3" 4×3 pdr 2×21" torpedo tubes
1×18" completed 6×21" torpedo tubes

Protection Belt 3"–2" Bulkheads 3"–2" Barbettes 7"–4"–3" Turrets 13"–11"–7"–4.5"

Machinery Parsons geared turbines s.h.p. 90,000 31.32 knots 4 screws 18 Yarrow small tube boilers
Furious Brown & Curtis geared turbines s.h.p. 94,000 31.5 knots 4 screws 18 Yarrow small tube boilers

Fuel 3,160 tons oil

Radius 3,200 at 19 knots

Complement 880

Fate
Courageous Converted to aircraft carrier 1924–8. Torpedoed and sunk by U-29 22 September 1939, 515 men lost.
Glorious Converted to aircraft carrier 1924–30. Sunk by German battlecruisers *Scharnhorst* and *Gneisenau* off Norway, 8 June 1940; over 800 men lost.
Furious Converted to aircraft carrier 1921–5. Sold and broken up at Troon, January 1948.

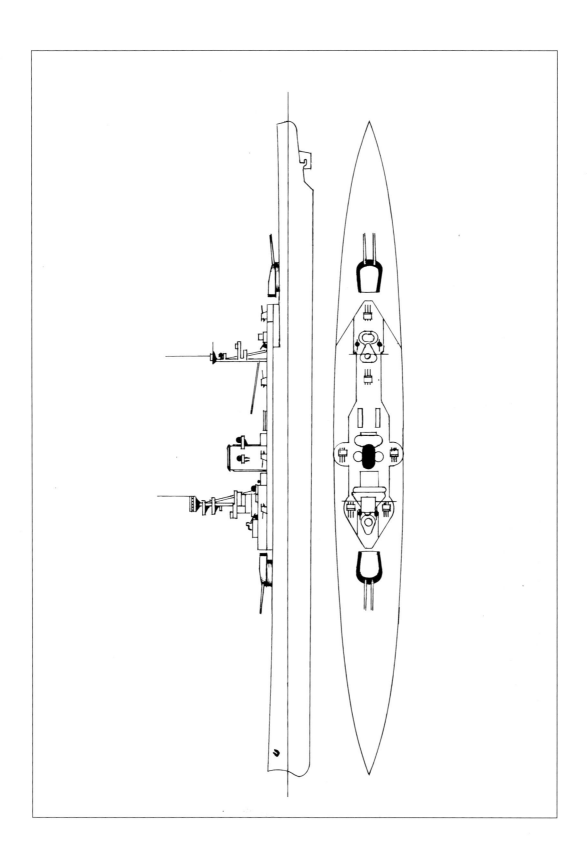

HOOD Class (Battlecruiser, Emergency War Programme)

Ship	Built at	Laid down	Launched	Completed
Hood	Clydebank	01/09/16	22/08/18	Mar. 1920
Anson	Armstrongs	09/11/16		
Howe	Cammell Laird	16/10/16		
Rodney	Fairfield	09/10/16		

Dimensions 860'×104'×28.5'

Displacement 41,200 tons   45,200 tons deep load

Armament 8×15"   12×5.5"   4×4"   4×3 pdr   6×12" torpedo tubes

Protection Belt 12"–7"–5"   Bulkheads 5"–4"   Barbettes 12"–6"–5"   Turrets 15"–11"–5"   Conning Tower 11"–9"

Machinery Brown-Curtis geared turbines s.h.p. 144,000   32 knots   4 screws   24 Yarrow small tube boilers

Fuel 4,000 tons oil

Radius 6,300 at 12 knots

Complement 1,477

Fate

Hood — Sunk by magazine explosion during gun action with *Bismarck* and *Prinz Eugen* in the Denmark Strait, 24 May 1941, 1,338 men perished.

Anson — Construction halted 9 March 1917. Contract cancelled 17 March 1919.

Howe — Construction halted 9 March 1917. Contract cancelled 17 March 1919.

Rodney — Construction halted 9 March 1917. Contract cancelled 17 March 1919.

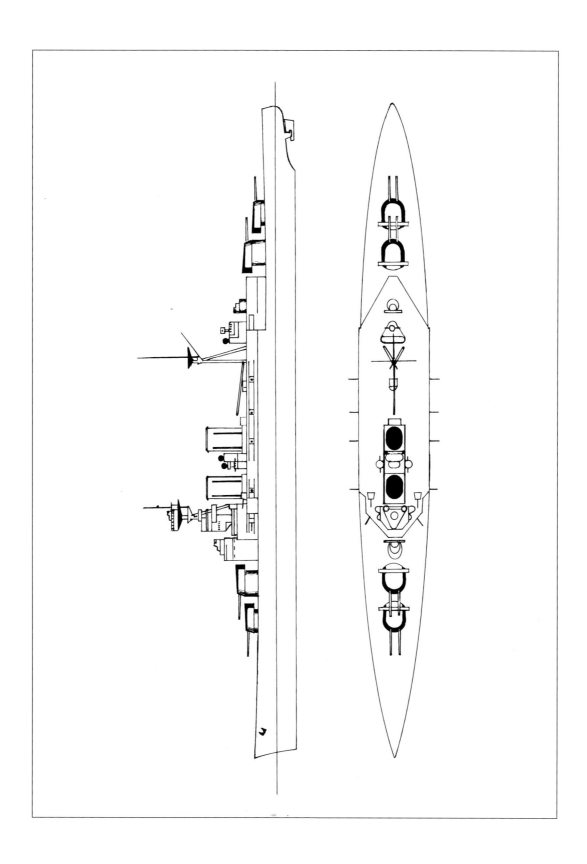

BIBLIOGRAPHY

Attwood, E.L. *War-Ships*, Longmans, Green and Co., London, 1912.

Brown, D.K. *A Century of Naval Construction*, Conway Maritime Press, London, 1983.

Burt, R.A., and Trotter, W.P. *Battleships of the Grand Fleet: A Pictorial Review of the Royal Navy's Capital Ships in World War One*, Arms and Armour Press, London, 1982.

Burt, R.A. *British Battleships of World War One*, Arms and Armour Press, London, 1986.

Campbell-Holmes, A. *Practical Shipbuilding*, 2 vols, Longmans, Green and Co., London, 1st edition 1904, 2nd edition 1908, new impressions 1914, 1916, 1917, 1918.

Gordon, A. *The Rules of the Game: Jutland and the British Naval Command*, John Murray, London, 1996.

Hume, J.R. and Moss M.S. *Beardmore: The History of a Scottish Industrial Giant*, Heinemann, London, 1975.

Kennedy, P. *The Rise of Anglo-German Antagonism, 1860–1914*, Allen and Unwin, London, 1980.

Lorenz, E.H. *Economic Decline in Britain: The Shipbuilding Industry 1890–1970*, Oxford University Press, 1991.

Mackay, R.F. *Fisher of Kilverstone*, Clarendon Press, Oxford, 1973.

Marder, A. *From Dreadnought to Scapa Flow: The Royal Navy in the Fisher Era, 1904–1914*, Oxford University Press, 1964.

McDermaid, N.J. *Shipyard Practice as Applied to Warship Constructions*, Longmans, Green and Co., London, 1911.

Morris, A.J. *The Scaremongers: The Advocacy of War and Re-armament, 1896–1914*, Routledge, Kegan and Paul, London, 1984.

Moss, M., and Russell, I. *Range and Vision: The First Hundred Years of Barr and Stroud*, Mainstream Press, 1994.

Parkes, Oscar. *British Battleships*, Seeley, London, 1957.

Peebles, H.B. *Warshipbuilding on the Clyde: Naval Orders and the Prosperity of the Clyde Shipbuilding Industry, 1889–1939*, John Donald, Edinburgh, 1990.

Ranft, B. *Technical Change and British Naval Policy*, London, 1995.

Reid, A. 'The Division of Labour in the British Shipbuilding Industry 1880–1920', PhD thesis, Cambridge University, 1980.

Roberts, J. *The Battle-cruiser Hood*, Conway Maritime Press, London, 1983.

—— *The Battleship Dreadnought*, Conway Maritime Press, London, 1992.

Sumida, T. *In Defence of Naval Supremacy: Finance, Technology and British Naval Policy, 1880–1914*, Hymans, London, 1989.

Thearle, S.P. *The Modern Practice of Shipbuilding in Iron and Steel*, 2 vols, Collins, London, 1910.

Trebilcock, C. *The Vickers Brothers: Armaments and Enterprise 1854–1914*, Europa Publications, London, 1977.

Warren, K. *Armstrongs of Elswick*, Macmillan, London, 1990.

Watton, R. *The Battleship Warspite*, Conway Maritime Press, London, 1988.

DREADNOUGHT BIBLIOGRAPHY

Ship's Covers

The National Maritime Museum, The Old Brass Foundry, Woolwich Arsenal.
Dreadnought ships' covers: Dreadnought, Orion Class, King George V Class, Iron Duke Class, Queen Elizabeth Class, Royal Sovereign Class, HMS *Agincourt*, HMS *Erin*.

Dreadnought Ship's Plans

HMS *Orion*, HMS *Iron Duke*, HMS *Queen Elizabeth*, HMS *Tiger*, HMS *Royal Sovereign*, HMS *Hood*.

Visual Bibliography

The Business Record Centre, 3 Thurso Street, University of Glasgow, Glasgow G11 6PE.
John Brown, Clydebank, Collections:
HMAS *Australia* UCS1/116/5.
HMS *Inflexible* UCS1/116/213.

HMS *Tiger* UCS1/116/10 and UCS1/116/11 (98 images).
HMS *Barham* UCS1/116/12, UCS1/116/13, UCS1/116/14, UCS1/116/15, UCS1/116/16 (253 images).
HMS *Repulse* UCS1/116/17, UCS1/116/18, UCS1/116/19, UCS1/116/20, UCS1/116/21, UCS1/116/22 (344 images).
HMS *Hood* UCS1/116/24, UCS1/116/25, UCS1/116/26, UCS1/116/27, UCS1/116/28, UCS1/116/29, UCS1/116/30 (412 images).
Illustrated brochure, John Brown, Clydebank Shipyard and Engineering Works, *c.* 1910, UCS1/115/17.
Illustrated Brochure, John Brown and Co., *c.* 1919, UCS1/115/26.
Beardmore, Parkhead and Dalmuir albums:
UGD100/1/11/1, UGD100/1/11/2, UGD100/1/11/4, UGD100/1/11/7.

INDEX

Ship names are in italic script. All names are HM Ships unless otherwise stated. Illustration captions and the Appendix are included in the index.

Agincourt 3, 13, 88, 117, 166–7
Ajax 154–5
Alfred Herbert Ltd, Coventry 14
Almirante Cochrane (Chilian Navy) 3, 168
Almirante Latorre (Chilian Navy) 168
Amalgamated Society of Engineers (ASE) 14
Anson 174
apprentices 10, 14, 29, 31, 32
armoured plate 11–12, 18, 19–22, 39–41
Armstrong Whitworth ix, 2, 3, 6, 11, 12, 14, 31, 74, 76, 106–8, 117
Arrol cranes 26, 56, 83, 84
Atlas Steel Works, Sheffield 18, 20, 23, 100
Attwood, E.L. (naval constructor) 6, 7
Audacious 154–5
Australia 146–7

Babcock and Wilcox 15, 74, 98
barbettes 40, 43, 78, 79
Barham ix, 3, 15, 46, 47, 78–81, 88, 116, 120–1, 122, 160–1
Barr and Stroud 15, 76, 109
Battleship Dreadnought, The, J.M. Roberts 27
Beardmore x, 3, 8, 12, 15, 16, 17, 19–22, 24–5, 29, 74, 76, 85, 99, 101–5
Bellerophon 4, 68, 69, 130, 140–1

Bellerophon class 3, 88
Benbow 8, 156–7
Boilermakers' Society (USBISS) 15, 24, 29, 30, 31–2
boilers 15, 95, 98
Brassey's Naval and Shipping Annual 19
briefs, ship's 6–7
Brown and Curtis turbines 15, 88
building costs 1, 3–4

Cammell Laird 3, 11, 14, 15
Canada 3, 88, 117, 168–9
Carlisle Agreement 1902 15
caulking 30
Centurion 154–5
Churchill, Winston, First Lord of the Admiralty (1911–15) 6, 71, 132
closed shop 15
Clyde Workers' Committee 15
Clydebank ix, x, 8, 16, 21, 23, 26, 27, 29, 42, 54, 59, 78–88, 94–7, 122, 123, 126–7
Collingwood 142–3
Colossus 148–9
Conqueror 150–1
construction times 4–5
costs 1, 3–4
Courageous (aircraft carrier) 15, 172–3
Coventry Ordnance 14

Dalmuir x, 15, 16, 17, 19, 24–5, 33, 46, 56, 57

demarcations 27–8, 29, 75
Devonport Dockyard ix, 3, 8
D'Eyncourt, Eustace (DNC 1912–24) 6
Director of Naval Construction (DNC) 5–7, 12
drawing office 17
drawings, ship's 6–8
Dreadnought ix, 1, 4, 5, 7, 36, 50–1, 64–5, 66, 67, 88, 130–1, 136–7
Dreadnought programme 1

Eagle (aircraft carrier) 168
Emperor of India 8, 156–7
Erin 3, 88, 164–5
establishment lists 34
Excellent (Naval Gunnery School) 117–19

Fairfield 2, 3, 12, 14, 26, 31, 32
family work gangs 28, 30, 34
Froude, R.E., Admiralty Experimental Works 10
Furious (aircraft carrier) 6, 15, 88, 172

Glorious (aircraft carrier) 6, 15, 26, 172–3
Glorious class 6, 88
gun barrels 14, 79, 82–3, 85–6, 101–8, 110–13
gunnery inspection 117–19

Hadfield Projectiles 14

Harland and Wolff 3, 15, 26
Haslar, Admiralty experimental
    tank 6, 10–11
Hawthorn, Leslie 15
Hecla Works, Sheffield 76
Hercules 148-9
Hood ix, 1, 5, 15, 27, 38, 39,
    40–1, 59, 86, 87, 88, 124–5,
    126–7, 174–5
Howe 174

Indefatigable 3, 146–7
Indefatigable class 5, 88
Indomitable 138–9
Inflexible 138–9
Invincible 138–9
Iron Duke 12, 52, 70, 71, 72, 73,
    75, 156–7
Iron Duke class 1, 6, 8, 88

Jane's Fighting Ships 12, 15
John Brown 2, 3, 4, 5, 11, 14, 15,
    16, 18, 59, 74
John Brown photographs ix, x,
    116
Jutland, Battle of 133–4

keel plates 26, 37, 38
King George V 60–1, 62, 63, 154–5
King George V class 1, 3, 6, 8, 88
Krupps and Harvey armour
    plate 19

Lion 90–1, 152–3
Lion class 5, 5–6, 6, 88
lock outs 31, 32

Malaya 3, 11, 88, 160–1
Marlborough 156–7
models 6, 10–11
Monarch 108, 150–1
mould lofts 8–9, 10, 16
Munitions Act 1907 14, 15, 33

Narbeth, J.H. (naval constructor)
    5, 10

National Maritime Collection ix
Neptune 6, 15, 55, 88, 144–5
New Zealand 3, 146–7

Orion 12, 150–1
Orion class 1, 3, 5, 6, 7, 88
overtime 4, 7, 30, 34
Palmers ix, 3, 31, 32, 33
Parkhead, gun works 14, 19–22,
    101–5
Parsons 15, 74, 88–91, 94, 97
petitions, Royal Dockyard 34, 75
piece rates 14, 28, 29, 30–2
plate
    armoured 10–11, 18–22
    wastage 11
plating 27–8
Portsmouth Dockyard ix, 1, 3, 4,
    7–8, 15, 36, 50–1, 55, 58,
    60–1, 62, 63, 64–5, 66–73, 74,
    130–1
Princess Royal 112, 128–9, 152–3
profits 3

Queen Elizabeth 3, 4, 5, 11, 37, 52,
    63, 74, 75, 76, 88, 100,
    117–19, 160–1
Queen Elizabeth class 1, 3, 6, 7,
    27, 75, 88
Queen Mary 152–3

Ramillies 4, 14, 56, 57, 162–3
Renown 5, 15, 43, 45, 170–1
Renown class 6, 88
Repulse 5, 15, 42, 43, 45, 54,
    81–4, 116, 117, 124–5, 170–1
Reshadieh (Ottoman Navy) 3, 164
Resolution 4, 162–3
Revenge 4, 112, 162–3
Rio de Janeiro (Brazilian Navy) 3, 166
River Don Works 11, 14, 110–11
riveting 28–9, 44
Rodney 174
Royal Oak 4, 162–3
Royal Sovereign ix, 4, 58, 162–3
Royal Sovereign class ix, 27, 88

St Vincent 142–3
St Vincent class 3, 88
Scotts 2, 3, 15, 19
shells 14, 114–15, 118
Shipbuilding Employers'
    Federation (SEF) 31, 32
Shipwrights' and
    Shipconstructors' Association
    (SSA) 15, 31, 33
Silk and Cribb, photographers ix,
    x, 55
specifications 6–7
steel plate 10–11
strikes 31–2
Sultan Osman I (Ottoman Navy) 3,
    166
Superb 140–1

Temeraire 140–1
tendering, competitive 3
Thames Iron Works 3
Thunderer 150–1
Tiger 6, 48, 54, 85, 88, 158–9
trade unions 15, 30–5
trials 76–7, 116–19, 122, 123–5
turbines 15, 88–91, 94, 97

Valiant 2, 3, 8, 88, 160–1
Vanguard 5, 89, 142–3
Vickers 2, 7, 11, 14, 19, 74
Vickers, Barrow-in-Furness ix,
    88–93, 112–15, 128–9

wage agreements 14, 29, 30, 31,
    31–2, 33
Wallsend Slipway Engineering
    Co. 74, 76, 98
Warspite 3, 4, 11, 88, 119, 160–1
Watts, Philip (DNC 1902–12) 6,
    6–7, 7
Weir, G.J., Cathcart 15, 74
women workers 14, 15, 33
work gangs x, 27–30, 76
workers' committees 14, 15
working hours 4, 15, 34, 75
workshop movement 14